Mental as Anything:

The Collective

Grant Budge

AUTHENTIC LIFE

© Copyright 2021

Grant Budge (First Publication)

ISBN 978-1-83-823661-8

A copy of the CIP report for this book is available from the British Library.

Authentic Life is an imprint of Integrity Media Ltd, a UK publishing company.

www.integrity-media.co.uk

NOTE FROM THE PUBLISHER

Integrity Media is a publishing company focused on helping individuals who are or have suffered poor mental health to tell their stories; and in so doing help enable our authors to move forward and our readers to better understand the challenges of poor mental health for their own education and support. Therefore, books published by Integrity Media, including this one, contain mature themes, frequently relayed in an open and honest manner. To enable our readers to decide if this work may be suitable and/or appropriate for them, we provide a list below of such themes contained in this publication.

The following topics are listed here in order of importance:

Depression
Suicidal thoughts and proceedings
Addiction
Sexualisation
Miscarriage
Infidelity

The following topics are not discussed in the book but some references may trigger uneasiness from readers who have their own difficulties:

Eating habits / Eating disorders
Body dysmorphic disorder

NOTE FROM THE AUTHOR

This memoir addresses some unquestionably serious and difficult subjects. If you find yourself negatively affected in any way by its content, please seek help or support from one of the institutions established to help individuals dealing with poor mental health.

From my perspective, this work is intended as a transparent and honest narrative of my own experiences with poor metal health and my interpretation in hindsight of how I handled and overcame it. It is presented with the genuine hope that, by increasing the ever-evolving society dialogue and understanding of mental health, both those suffering from it and the actors that precipitate it can learn and grow. So that we can all collectively, continuously, make tomorrow a better day for everyone.

Acknowledgements

I would like to thank my editor, Alicia Violet. Her scrutiny, guidance and support exceeded my expectations and helped me finalise what was an especially challenging project for me. In my opinion, it may be said that the sign of a good editor is one that helps make their author's voice sharper, clearer and better. Alicia, you certainly enabled me to do that. Thank you.

This book is dedicated to my wife, without whose love my life would be absent of so much.

CONTENTS

Prologue: The Darkness

It feels like the world is becoming a dark and hostile place of humanity's making. The numerous traits of decline might frequently be veiled by sugar-coated smiles, but the underlying menace persists and spreads like a virus. Commercialism has driven a 'want' society at any cost, quashing any determination of 'need'. Far too many people take before they give. Greed, jealousy and envy are steadily becoming the cornerstones of societal behaviour in western civilisation. It is a disappointing observation that inevitably drives a subdued and vulnerable mind to a singular query: if death is inevitable, why endure the subversive malice?

MENTAL QUAGMIRE

Opening my eyes, I see the endless ocean stretching away from the shore. Its majesty witnessed in slow motion as the advance of oncoming waves is impeded by the undertow of the ebbing tide. The impact of this unseen sub-surface force, also slow and relentless in sapping the strength from the weak and weightless wildlife that explores the foreshore, carrying them out into the fluid expanse. For those steadfast swash zone adventurers, the rip curl dissects the waves, offering a more perilous and accelerated passage away from the sanctuary off the land. Above the undulating liquid surface, the sun descends steadily, scorching the horizon and reflecting on the water. In this moment, optics gift the waves power to defy nature, seemingly caressing the sun's corona, quenching it in preparation for the dark chill of the night.

The secluded cove I occupy is empty. Behind me, the rocky escarpment ascends into the sky, obscuring my presence from the world beyond. I am alone. No one here to witness or interfere in my closing act. Isolation gifting me the autonomy to function as actor, director and producer of this endgame and complete my part in humanity's eternal play. I stand facing the open water. My clothes are neatly stacked in an orderly fashion behind me. The cooling night air envelops my naked body, seeking to awaken my senses, begging for reconsideration. I feel nothing. My mind is resolute. This is not a whimsical act. I didn't suddenly wake up this morning with a new agenda. The path was long, the journey jagged with ceaseless deliberation. I have fought in vain with external forces and with myself to find a place where I would feel in accord with the world around me. A perceived struggle that failed to deliver me a state of being where I fit harmoniously within society and, by association, a failure to find acceptance for who I am. In a world that desires explanation of everything and through such need endorses the categorisation of humanity by mass segmentation around behavioural conventions, the outlier becomes the outcast. After obstinately pursuing acceptance like a child pursues the affections of a parent for one thousand eight-hundred and twenty-five days, I can but only accept my 'outlier' fate. If I have achieved nothing else during this protracted, unobserved crusade, it is that I know in my soul every opportunity has been attempted with fresh-faced enthusiasm. But no matter how strong a person's zeal, at some point in the absence of good fortune, the will can be broken. Standing here tonight, I knew I had given my life everything I had to offer, but society had repeatedly judged me to be found wanting. So much so that optimism had been sucked from my spirit and now every future eventuality I can conceive plays out in my head to the same dismal end. With such prophecy only a masochist would continue to endure such endeavours. I am not such a person. I need to feel less, because everyday hurts too much. And no path will bring equivalent reprieve from the anguish I feel than the one in action at this moment.

The soft soles of my feet feel the coarseness of the shingle beneath them, angular stone edges jutting skyward, desperate to draw blood. I step forward to allow the icy water to envelop my feet and numb my nerves. In this moment, as a child, I would have retreated joyously back up the beach, shrieking with delight. Tonight though, the anesthetising chill is nature's invitation. It is an enticement for me to plunge in and be released from the torment that has consumed me. It is as if nature knew the persistent and ever-swelling confusion that had swamped my mind and pressurised my skull, offering me the depths of its freezing water as a kindness. I know the time will shortly arrive that I will wade farther out into the swelling darkness, steadily immersing myself until only the air in my lungs provides life-preserving buoyancy. But for this brief moment, I stand without fear and savour the immense beauty this world has to offer. Maybe my only real failure was to expect that my life should have mattered more. To believe that amidst all this wonder the insignificant organism that I am could have made a difference, could have been needed, could have been noticed, could have been indispensable. It is a sad commentary on my existence that it is only now, in this moment, that I can finally accept the averageness of my contribution, as a result of my imposed societal 'outlier' designation.

Closing my eyes again, I take a deep breath, but there is no cold night air to fill my lungs. Instead, tepid air tainted with the smell of damp is drawn through my nostrils. I reopen my eyes to see the inside of the bathroom door. I was daydreaming. To my left, a heated rack holds three wet towels, and I can see the remnants of the suspended mist created by the shower. In an instant, my thoughts of numbing comfort are gone and all my negative emotions are released as if through a flood gate. I am home. Through the wood panelled door, I hear my wife crying and I am dragged abruptly back to reality. Reacquainted with the anxiety in my head, I take a breath, open the door and step out into the hallway. Words have failed me once tonight already and I dare not risk degenerating the situation further. With a soft caress as I pass by her, I descend the stairs. She follows me, and after thirty years together, I know she is struggling to admit her observational role in this evolving tragedy. Struggling to understand why external judgement affects me so much. She is unable to accept the simple truth that an individual's measure of success today is calendar constraint to the here and now through a digitally-connected world searching for immediate daily recognition. The longer a person exists outside of this congratulatory data stream, the more they become marginalised and are deemed inconsequential. This is the world that greets me every morning. In this world I feel completely lost. Shamed by the frequent virtual posts of triumph and joy from friends and colleagues. I feel like a ghost to those around me. If I wasn't actually here, who would notice? *Hope is the greatest depressant*. That is the thought that resonates in my head, taunting me and challenging me to concede.

While my wife doesn't completely comprehend the foundations of my hopelessness, she has acknowledged its existence and has endeavoured to elevate my mind through the philosophies of others. She has cited the Latin proverb 'fortune favours the brave', Ernest Hemmingway's doctrine that 'everyone is the architect of their own luck'; and whether it was her motto to claim, Jane Fonda's slogan 'no pain no gain' from her 1980s exercise routines. But the truth is that my character has never been rallied by soundbites of positivity and, as such, these phrases have become uncomfortable companions to my frayed psyche, feeling like further judgements rather than inspirational statements that are increasingly drowned out by the relentless drumming in my head: *Hope is the greatest depressant*.

There are numerous events that have guided me to the depth of despair I now occupy. Yet, at the top of the pile would have to be the one-hundred and sixty-five job applications spread across one-hundred and fifty-six weeks. Each application having been crafted with care, tailored to meet formulaic criteria set out by recruitment consultants and head-hunters, today's invited gatekeepers of the working world. One hundred and sixty-five job applications against which I was judged to be found wanting or simply dismissed without review. And with every emailed *'Thank you for taking the time to apply for the position, but...'*, finding it harder to steel myself to repel the ever-swelling beat: *hope is the greatest depressant.*

With her persistently optimistic support, Jenny had once asked why I let the opinions of these faceless people get to me so much. Good question. A question that in answer to my rationale mind repeatedly informs me that I am just being judged by an algorithm or by a young adult fresh from university and void of experience in the sector I operate within. So my predicament may really be just a function of the system and not me. But then following such thoughts, I inevitably consider probability theory and the full weight of the skewed negative bias I am experiencing lands like a dead, suffocating mass on my chest.

Opening the front door, I turn to look at Jenny one last time, feign a smile and leave. In many ways it is unfathomable how I find myself sitting in my car, staring through the windscreen in disbelief. Disbelief not of the ethereal burning sunset steadily torching the horizon, but of how easily I had just walked out of the house. Astonished at how readily I had again thrown in the towel, without even the slightest attempt at explaining the depth of my despair to her. Leaving Jenny standing in the doorway, sobbing. I had never done anything like that before and I have no right to. Unconsciously slamming the door with such frustration that an observer would assume I was the wronged party. How distant from the truth that was. Jenny is perfection. She has surrendered her soul to me throughout the twenty-five years of our marriage and the five years of courting that preceded it. She has loved unconditionally and sometimes, for my part, without reciprocation. Yes, she has made mistakes, minor glitches in an otherwise serene existence. But they have always been acknowledged. Addressed. Faced up to. Explained and apologised for. That is one of her most beautiful traits, self-diagnosis and admonishment when in error. It isn't always rapid in delivery, but when it arrives, it is unequivocal and exposed. Laid bare. Vulnerable. In this instant though, she had done nothing except having the misfortune to be mine. She didn't even know what the problem was. How could she, when even I would persistently fail to define it to myself?

Turning the key in the ignition, I put the car into gear and reversed out of the driveway. Earlier in the day I had agreed to meet a few of my friends at the pub. Whether it had been a subconscious action pre-empting what was going to transpire with Jenny, I didn't know. What I had known was that I needed to talk to someone and was grateful that it would be them. They were always there for me. And while every discussion with them began as an inaudible cacophony, through gradual iteration sense eventually emerged, opinions were respectfully aired, and actions defined.

The pub was only a five-minute drive away and I soon found myself pulling into a parking space outside. Getting out of the car, I walked across the tarmac and entered. Inside, the décor was that of a traditional country inn. Booths lined in blue fabric, mismatched wooden chairs and tables, aged oak floorboards, with a fire in the centre of the left-hand wall radiating a wondrous dancing glow. The lighting was dim and soft music was playing to compliment the comforting ambience. Unlike most pubs these days, it was a free house, independently managed by a young couple who enjoyed offering new beers to their customers. It would be fair to say that not all new draught additions from adventurous flavouring micro-breweries had been well received, but the potluck variety had become something of a legend that added to the pub's charm and acted like a magnet to the local community. Such was the pub's status that the establishment was never unoccupied. Across the lounge, to the right of the fire, I spied Lizzie. She was sitting alone at a round booth, looking slightly despondent, cradling what appeared to be a gin and tonic. At that moment, she looked up, smiled and waved at me. I waved back, then pointed to the bar, where I went to buy a pint of the latest guest beer.

NEWT THE STRONG

Lizzie Newton was oddly named by her parents after a Korean cartoon creation about a Victorian English mystery novelist who solved crimes. The graphic novel character had written a serialisation for a gentleman's magazine, loved collecting books and conducting chemical experiments. From birth, the name and direct comparison had been perfect for Lizzie. Her namesake had been published in the magazine under the fictional authorship of Logica Docens. *The pseudonym had probably been selected to conjure masculine imagery and thereby gift professional and social acceptance, in much the same way Mary Ann Evans, the Brontë sisters and Nelle Harper had accomplished before her. Yet the name was also a play on words.* Logica Docens *was the Latin for the legitimate doctrine to learn through study. It was a rudimentary doctrine that every assertion can only be true or false, and not both; and that through iterative study of logic, the foundations of any assertion may be revealed. This was also how Lizzie, the real one, pursued life. She questioned everything. Interrogated almost. Believed life was a sequence of binary decisions that could be amalgamated progressively into a detailed algorithm for modelling and understanding human nature. Then, armed with that insight, life may be piloted to optimum effect. The only issue with her hypothesis or assertion was that, reinforced by her own experience, she always failed to account for the influence of her personal judgement bias, exposing her to the risk of simply reinforcing her own beliefs. She saw what she wanted to see. That said, she always provided a robust framework to any of our group's deliberations. Which is why we rarely called her by her Christian name.*

Instead, she was simply 'Newton' or 'Newt', in subtle acknowledgement of her superior intellect.

As with the structured nature of her mind, she always dressed in authoritarian outfits. Power suits. Trousers and blouse combinations. Rarely wearing skirts. No stilettos. Always flat shoes or simple stub heels of no more than one inch. Practical footwear to the extreme. Her makeup was always delicate, lightly accentuating her features, unlike the throng of women forced to remove their face nightly for fear of leaving it on the pillowcase. Her eyes were hazel and sparkled when she smiled. At five foot six inches, she was just above average height for a female. With a slim build maintained by a reasonable level of exercise post triple pregnancies, she was the epitome of the middle-aged woman teenagers inappropriately fantasised about.

Despite her logical formula for life, she considered herself a realist. While she saw all decisions as noughts and ones, she appreciated that successful navigation was about getting the right question to be asked. More specifically, Newt's greatest ability was to get people to ask the right question that led to the outcome she believed optimal. She was either a consummate influencer or a manipulator depending on your perspective. Due to her Northern Irish heritage, this 'influencing' had on occasions been taken as curt, earning her the repeated reputation as 'the Bitch' with work colleagues. But she refused to let that inhibit her, wearing the nickname like a badge of honour instead. After all, she would say, 'Isn't doggedness the attribute of every successful human being?' It was certainly one applauded and admired when exhibited by a man as he strives to ascend to the highest echelons of the corporate hierarchy.

Her work ethic was intense. Resolution of emails bracketed her waking hours. At work on Christmas day if required. Travelling at weekends if required. She appreciated that executive corporate culture held expectations and that perception was all too frequently used to infer sixty percent of a person's belief system. To survive, she knew it wasn't just what she did but how hard people believed she worked to deliver it. It was a game and she played it well.

As a friend, Newt could sometimes act in a way that made it momentarily challenging to like her. Dispensing and framing realities factually and concisely from her own point of view, completely overlooking that while from her detached position accepting her perspective may seem functional, even natural, it was not always the case for the person trapped in the scenario. I used to be reluctant to solicit her council because of this almost surgical approach. These days though, with my emotions suppressed, I am able to receive her forensic challenge with a constant and steady pulse. It seems like my depression-driven emotional numbness has yielded one benefit after all: a heightened emotional threshold.

Her sharp rhetoric, she had once explained, was a product of her youth and regional heritage. As one of five Belfast siblings, four sisters and a lone brother, raised in a terrorised city during the '70s and '80s, there had never been room for ambiguity. She always professed that the genetic makeup of the time was for conversations which were brutally honest and ruthless in their narrative. She would sometimes claim that thick skin and viperous tongues were national characteristics of the Northern Irish, that issued harsh perspectives on life, as a result of the dystopian society they had been distilled in. However, despite the circumstances of her birthplace, Newt's family, with the support of God, had remained true to the beliefs of Christianity. Armed with religion, they had retained a safe distance from the slippery slope of subversive behaviour. Every day had presented danger, direct and indirect, but their continued existence within such a crucible of anger and hatred had normalised the risks. Newt's husband believed it was this forging of her personality that precipitated the composed approach she took in her work. While all would panic around her, she always stood calm in the battlefield, elevating herself to understand the dysfunctional situation that had emerged and disassemble it so it could be rebuilt with stability. It was easy to misinterpret this composed and direct rhetoric as a coldness in Newt's character, but that would be inaccurate. While she never suffered fools, she brimmed with affection and love for friends and family. The depth of this love was never more present than when witnessed by her husband's side. They were love cats. Completely lost in each other and had been that way since the very beginning.

It was also her Northern Irish heritage and developed composure which forged an internal strength and bravery that few saw, because of her petite beauty. She had once told me that, in her childhood, her family had considered her to be weak, quiet and in a world of her own. 'Away with the fairies' as people said in Belfast. Maybe she could have been externally perceived that way for a number of years. After all, she had a sister two years her junior who had felt compelled to stand up and fight her elder sibling's battles, threatening to beat girls up if they didn't leave Newt alone. Newt had also told me how she had once been chased down the road by a dog when she was a child. The dog bit at her wellington boot to get a hold of her. Newt had simply shaken the boot off and run to her house in socks, screaming. But that wasn't who she was inside. And as she grew into her teenage years, an inner resolve had emerged. A girl with quiet confidence who had fled through a graveyard to avoid a skirmish between the IRA and the British military. A girl who had drunkenly sneaked back into the house late at night and managed to sell sobriety to her parents. The weak, quiet and daydreaming girl who announced with zeal, at the age of seventeen, that she wanted to attend university in England, the 'country of pagans and heathens', as her great aunt Briege used to say.

Now Briege had been a Northern Irish stereotype, if ever there was one, a character and a half, who Newt's husband had shared many hours of banter with. When he had first met her, he had taken Briege's comments to heart, believing them to be genuine republican sentiments. She never restrained from issuing provocative opinions about the British. Everything was fair game. But politics and religion were her weapons of choice and, like a Yorkshire miner, her memory was long and sculpted from the disdain of her predecessors. Newt's husband had once been held to account for the great potato famine of 1845 to 1849. Then subjected to a torrent of praise for Guy Fawkes as having had the right idea to blow up Parliament. 'Ahead of his time!' Briege had once proclaimed with a smirk.

Newt had recounted to me the anecdote of how once, despite the frustration Briege raised in him, there was only a single instance when her husband's composure had failed him. The post had arrived one morning at their home in England and, with it, an envelope from Belfast. A small bundle of pamphlets espousing the Catholic faith and a handwritten note from Briege was sealed inside, simply reading: 'I'm sending these because you won't be able to get them in that Godless country'. The words had incensed him so much it had taken Newt a day to completely calm him. Her approach to the jib had been mellower and more sophisticated. She had put the bundle in the bin.

With the passage of time comes wisdom, and as the years progressed, Newt's husband had begun to see Briege's rhetoric for what it really was. Just banter. A test of his tenacity and worthiness. He had to be good enough for Newt. He couldn't be a shrinking violet if he was to survive a Northern Irish union. When he realised that was the case, *he played into it. Seizing every opportunity to demonstrate his worth. He started to play her game the same way: not only firing comments back to defend or justify, but to provoke in equal measure. Briege was quicker on the uptake than him though, and identified his shifting approach almost immediately. From that moment on, they held a mutually playful understanding which fed their dance of derision every time they were together. She was a real character and one he would never forget. Newt would never forget her either. She had grown up witnessing the Northern Irish way, including with her Aunt Briege, but had not necessarily appreciated it. But it may have been one of the sub-conscious elements that fertilised her desire to leave the native land and go to England to study. It was certainly this heritage that established the character I repeatedly sought for guidance.*

Gypsy Prophecy

I held my hand out to pocket the change from the barman then walked towards Newt. Sliding around the booth, I greeted her with a kiss on the cheek. "Hey, you," I said, "how you doing?"

"Better than you by the sounds of it!?" She replied light-heartedly, although her expression indicated concern. "You said you needed to talk. What's up? You and Jenny fighting again?"

"I just need a sanity break." I paused. "Life is a bit overwhelming."

"So why are you not talking about this with her? She's always been your bestie." Newt replied.

I sighed heavily. "It's hard."

"Much of life is." She responded matter-of-factly.

"It's at a point I can't talk with her. It's gone too far. Unspoken confessions that feel like they could destroy us." Newt remained silent. "At the moment, it's like everyone around me is moving forward and I'm standing still. Every day I see the gaps grow and don't know what to do to close them again."

"That's all in your head, you know. Everyone's lives are just different." Newt comforted.

"I know that, but I still need to feel like I'm evolving. Else what am I doing? What's the point of me?" I challenged her. "Every morning I put on the news to be confronted by stories and images of people who are contributing to the world. People making a difference!"

She interrupted. "You can't think like that!"

"Why not? Isn't it how the world thinks?" I knew I sounded desperate. "Everything is instantaneous. Including history. We are measured by what we have done today and yesterday at best. And what have I done?"

"It's starting to sound like you may be beyond my help and need professional support..." She sounded perturbed.

I lowered my head, swallowing her words in. I didn't know anymore.

Newt had been in my life for nearly fifteen years now. Most of that time she had witnessed my positivity, seen my strength and resilience. My joy for life. My capacity for love. After all, my overarching lifelong mantra had always been 'I love love'. Tonight though, I knew she was witnessing a different person. A person I knew to be almost bereft of all positive attributes, with a hollowed heart. A person stifled by their existence. I could tell that, because of my evident state of mind, she had decided her next words may hold more weight than ever before, so was retaining them sufficiently long enough to forge into something meaningful. Something that could reassure me. Provide me with strength. I chose to break the silence.

"You know, I was told by a fortune-teller two decades ago that I would have a period of misfortune in my work life. I hope every day now that this is it and that the end is in sight."

My words seemed to stall Newt's thinking further and she said nothing. So I rambled on.

"You know I've always been a pretty factual and practical person. I don't like ambiguity and, because of that, I'm not overtly superstitious. But I do harbour more than a passing interest in all aspects of the occult. There's just something in the mysticism and the unknown that draws me in!"

"I can appreciate that." Newt said calmly. "I think everyone feels that way at some point in their lives."

"I suppose so, but this is more than a passing fancy." I informed her. "In my home library, I have books ranging from psychic arts, palmistry and tarot, to dream interpretation, Shamanism, ceremonial magic, Wicca and Voodoo. I am not an expert in any of them, but I have grappled with the foundations of each vein of occultism and do embrace the connection they each endeavour to provide between the natural and unnatural."

"Unnatural?" Newt contested.

"I mean the unseen and unexplained." I clarified. Newt remained silent. "Anyway, it's probably because of this interest that I have approached with an open mind the prophecies of a handful of fortune tellers I have encountered during my life."

"You don't want to start seeking advice from clairvoyants. That's fortune cookie wisdom and zodiac speculation." She made her scepticism clear.

"I know what you mean. I accept that for the most part such prophetic wisdom is generic and clumsily patched together from observation and simple query. I know in general there are many charlatans who offer nothing more than a means to spend disposable income. They are at best mediocre mentalists."

"Exactly. I am so pleased you said that." Newt seemed relieved.

"There was one fortune teller though, the 'work misfortune' prognosticator, whose disclosures stood apart from the rest. She was specific and detailed." I paused and looked at Newt directly. "She predicted numerous events that have come to fruition. Including, I believe, this current hiatus of employment. Though she never said anything about how shit I would feel at the time."

"Hey, that's just a mindset you're in, it's not you!" I knew she was just trying to lighten my tone, so I chose not to comment.

"Have you ever been to New Orleans?" I asked suddenly.

Newt shook her head.

"Beautiful place! Well, some areas are beautiful. Jackson Square is one of those beautiful places. I think it's the definite must-do tourist location in New Orleans. It's conveniently nestled centrally on the French Quarter's riverfront. St Louis Cathedral dominates the vista on the north side of the square. It's a stunning third-generation Catholic sentinel from the late sixteenth century..." I momentarily sounded exuberant as I recalled its grandeur. Because while being British may leave me steeped daily in history, I remembered vividly how I had felt witnessing a building that had once sat at the heart of a new world settlement. "The main central tower dwarfs the rest of the frontal façade. It makes you feel like it is standing, watchful, over the saints and sinners that scurry before it every day. On either side of the main tower, two other conical towers reach majestically up to the sky, all in stark contrast to the spiritual folkways of the indigenous African decedents it serves."

"You're starting to sound a bit like a poet!" Newt joked but I let it wash over me, elevated above her humour within the comfort of my memories.

"Did you know the design of the square is based on the Place des Vosges in Paris? At its centre, a horseback statue of the seventh President of the United States, Andrew Jackson, marks the historic significance of the location, as the place where Louisiana formerly became part of the United States of America in 1803. And at its fore, towards the banks of the Mississippi, a row of handsome cabs always wait in pristine condition to transport tourists through time."

I took a moment, drawing in a long, wistful breath. Newt appeared to have decided to remain silent, aware that her previous remark had failed to elicit any response.

"It was where I met my oracle twenty years ago." Simultaneously, I witnessed a change in Newt's facial expression, finally grasping the reason for my historic preamble. "In contrast to the idyllic postcard picture elements of the square, around its perimeter, street artists and fortune tellers were plying for trade from the passing throngs. Like all the tourists, Jenny and I had to navigate around the gauntlet of continuous pleas for business. I was okay with that. I've always found it easy to decline pushy people."

Newt agreed and I continued.

"There was one, though, who sufficiently caught my attention to imagine paying ten dollars just to see what she had to say. There was also a bit of the *when-in-Las-Vegas-see-a-show* mentality." I glanced at Newt to see if she knew what I meant and she nodded. "Anyway, she hadn't heckled or made eye contact with anyone. She had just remained still, like she was in a trance. I don't know, maybe she thought custom would just come to her when it was destined to."

"Maybe she was just using telepathy to engage with customers!" Newt tested me again with another joke, but I let it pass once more without comment, immersed in my own narrative.

"Her head was adorned with this long scarf which vanished at the back underneath dark, scraggly hair. She had these mesmerising emerald eyes which were destroyed amidst a rainbow of eye shadow and too much mascara." I shook my head, unconsciously illustrating my disapproval. "She was a big woman as well."

"You can't say things like that these days!" Newt redressed me.

"I'm simply being factual! She had an abundant figure, which she attempted to conceal under this long-sleeved, baggy shirt and flowing skirt which clipped her ankles. Her clothing fabrics as well!" I proclaimed, unable to hide my disdain. "Stained by a pallet of pastel shades that did little to compliment her pale complexion!" I took a deep breath in before suddenly resuming my description with urgency, having just remembered additional details. "And her teeth! They were crooked and yellow, but surprisingly all accounted for." I flinched. "And then her fingers, stained from nicotine abuse, the skin dried from a life outdoors and weighed down by these ridiculously oversized rings. Honestly, she portrayed the gypsy queen to perfection."

"Is gypsy a politically correct term these days?" Newt couldn't help herself correcting me.

"I don't know, but I am with a friend, so I'm hoping you know I mean no offence. And I certainly don't need to feel any more judgment!" I hadn't spoken harshly, but I could see Newt had taken the rebuke to heart, so I gave her a weak appeasing smile before continuing.

"She was perched on a tiny, rickety wooden chair that seemed as though it could break at any moment and despatch her towards the paving. As soon as she knew she had caught my eye, she had gestured for me to sit and face her from the other side of a collapsible table."

The barman glanced over inquisitively for a moment and I waited for his attention to turn away from us before continuing.

"I remember she asked which was my dominant hand. Her voice was deeply southern, with this faint trace of French in her intonation. I wasn't sure what she meant, and she seemed to know I needed additional clarification so she told me she meant the one I wrote with. Without a word, I raised my right hand on to the table and she reached out with both her hands, resting her gnarled fingers on top of mine."

"Do you honestly believe in this kind of stuff?" Newt questioned.

"When I've finished. Tell me then that there is nothing in it." My voice was calm because I no longer required proof of the mystic, but Newt looked snubbed once again.

I continued my story. "I remember her saying that 'some charlatans' would tell me my left hand is the dominant one for males. Others that the left represents what I can achieve, and the right what I've done." I took a deep breath. "She'd spoken so softly when she claimed that it was 'all trash'. Then I remember her grasping my hand and twisting it palm to the sky. She studied it so intently! Her face snarled and eyes scrunched as her fingers traced the patchwork of creases. Her touch was really delicate. Not what I expected and, to be truthful, vaguely erotic!"

"Don't you start getting like Tif!" Tif was one of our other friends, who had issues of his own.

23

"She told me the hand is shaped in one of four ways. Each shape representing one of the four elements essential for life. Earth, air, water or fire. My hand is apparently shaped for fire." I paused, recalling how she had investigated every blemish. "She said people of fire are strong with energy. They are visionaries and have the ability to manifest what they see. But she warned me that with such strong imaginings an intolerance for suggestion can be nurtured. She told me to be vigilant in remaining open-minded."

'Remember to listen.' She had actually said, with a soft foreboding. Like she knew what was coming. I pondered for a moment what had happened next.

"I remember she had lowered her head at this point. All I could see was her headscarf. She was so close to me she could have easily smelt the fragrance of the last handwash I had used. It was all a bit disconcerting. She continued to tell me which lines represented my heart and my head. Observing that they were completely entwinned. Inseparable. 'Simian' she said. Apparently very rare! She said it meant that my head and heart worked in unison. Which I thought sounded like a positive attribute. And while she had initially said it was admirable, she went on to declare that it would inevitably bring me 'much anguish'."

"Cheerful psychic wasn't she?!" Newt quipped.

"She said people with a simian line find their logic and emotions hold singularity. They are strong with passion. They value fighting a just cause above the accrual of possessions and wealth. And they are averse to lies."

"Well, that certainly sounds true!"

"She also said I better be careful not to let conviction in my beliefs mature into pride, no one carries all of life's truths, we must remain open and alert to life's education."

"What did Jenny make of all of this?" Newt asked.

"She's a bit like me. She has an open mind, but up to that point I could tell she felt it was a little innocuous. However, that's when it all started to get more interesting. She traced the length of this curved line here...", I showed Newt the one I meant, the one that dissected my hand, "said I was content in love. And, at odds with my fire designation, had established control over my emotions."

"What? She suggested you were emotionally repressed?" Newt looked at me in disbelief.

"No. She just meant that people who are not intimidated by me find me stable and approachable. I think it is pretty accurate!" I waited a moment for Newt to comment further, but she remained quiet. "Then she pointed at all these crosses over my simian line. Said they represented how many dilemmas I would have in my life. Then she traced my life line here." I pointed at the line that arced from between my index finger and thumb at the top, down to the base of my thumb, just in case Newt didn't know which one I meant. "She said it is strongly curved, therefore reinforcing my fire. Because it is long and reaches round to the creases of my wrist, it symbolises my strength and enthusiasm for life. Then she pointed at this section here." Again, I identified the location on my palm for Newt. "She told me that here, where the line is broken, continued only by a patchwork of lines, that represented a period of suffering and uncertainty, possibly around my health. She was so concise in her interpretations. Functional and clinical. Unlike the earlier comments, she started to leave scant room for interpretation."

"And have you?" Newt asked.

"Have I what?"

"Had health issues?"

"Yes. Several." As with my gypsy, my concise response left little room for doubt. I continued, pointing again at my palm. "She told me this line represented my fate. Said it shows how much outside forces will influence my journey. The fact that my fate line begins at the base of my life line is a sign of independence. Which means my future is mine to command. But that, here," I pointed to my palm once more, "where my fate line intersects with my simian line, means my visions, my aspirations, will be affected by people around me who hold power to determine the outcomes of my actions, although I will most likely prevail in the long run. Even if the outcome may not be the end I originally envisaged, or so she said."

"Isn't that true for everyone though?" Newt criticised.

"Maybe. But like I said, wait until I have finished before judging, please!" I took a moment to regain my thoughts and then carried on with the story. "She told me my marriage line is strong and long, but that here, where it spawns a new track, a big event of some sort will most likely occur in that journey."

"I think every couple can lay claim to something like that in their relationship." Newt critiqued again.

"She told me I would have three children, but that she saw a fourth line that was uncertain." I waited for Newt to acknowledge what I had revealed.

"That's a bit more tangible I guess." She obliged.

"She then started to probe around this protrusion at the base of my thumb. Told me it is called the Venus mound. I have a large one, it indicates a spirit that frequents gratification, maybe even 'promiscuity'. I'm using her words by the way. She said I had a strong thumb, which meant I was practical. That I am good with money and I keep my promises."

At that moment, I spotted a lady staring over from a table on the other side of the room. I looked back waiting for her to avert her gaze before continuing.

"Then, with a sense of urgency, she clutched my ring finger. I flinched, half excepting her to slip my wedding band off and scarper, but she'd clasped my finger firm, and told me my ring finger arched lightly towards my middle finger. This apparently shows the strength of love I have for my for family." I took a shallow breath. "And with that she released my hand and fell silent. I waited for her to say something more, but her silence persisted. As did mine, because her expression had this look, like she was considering a final remark. I was right. She went on to tell me that palm lines on their own can only reveal so much. Consideration of the hand as a whole reveals so much more. That's when it got really freaky! She said she saw a sadness in my early life. An event that would hit me hard and would shape me. She told me she saw a struggle for personal success. A fight for a goal or goals of my own making which would bring a time of disturbance to what I felt was important to achieve. That doubt would take hold. And that when that time came I should remember my fire. Then she looked at me straight in the eye and said my life would be 'continuously bathed with femininity'. Told me it was a constant for me. And that was it."

"Did you ask her what she meant by that? 'Bathed in femininity'?"

"No. It didn't feel right and, to be honest, I was a bit unnerved by that point. Don't forget I am a little superstitious. I am cautious about this stuff. The way she looked, I thought if she wanted to tell me more she would have. So I thanked her, paid and we left."

"What did Jenny think of it all?"

"Like me, she took it with a cautious pinch of salt at the time. It's when we look back now that we see how eerie the whole thing was."

"Explain?"

"Well, there have been many times since that day, I have draped thoughts of my life over those proclamations like tracing paper to see if the interpretation of her remarks recorded in my mind mirrored the life I am living. On numerous occasions, I have identified truth in her words. Correlation beyond coincidence. So much so that I reached a point it became hard to ignore it."

Newt remained silent and, as I looked around the bar, I reflected on how I had ignored the gypsy's guidance and let my fire be dampened. How I had let events conspire to smother and suppress the furnace that once raged at my core. How I had allowed life to become a cacophony that prevented rational thought and made me hanker daily for night-time, and the reprieve and escape that slumber brought. As predicted, missed goals and doubt had landed repeatedly with conviction throughout my life and I have felt increasingly ill-equipped to navigate ways forward.

I knew my story had unsettled Newt. Having initially confessed to feelings of uncertainty in my life, I had suddenly relayed my prophetic story, which implied I had also conceded my destiny to the hands of nature or the spirits. Newt was rarely short for words, but this was one such time. We sat in silence listening to the jukebox.

CONFESSION

For all the time I have known Newt, she has always been an avid reader of self-help books. I could argue that they offered no better foundation for guidance than the mysticism I courted in New Orleans, but she would contest that and say they were books about positivism. She had told me once that she believed little in life was new to the world, just new to us as individuals; so she could grow indirectly by reading and learning about other people's experiences. She believed it enabled her to see her own encounters through the lens of someone who had gone before her, thereby identifying expedient frameworks for understanding any situation she found herself in, allowing her to adapt her behaviour. I could imagine that in her mind she was probably consulting her memories for a scenario that she could lean on to navigate the current situation. But rather than wait in silence, I chose to try and aid her with her mental blockage and turned the conversation back to the here and now.

"I just feel like I am in a hole and each day the sides get steeper. I don't sleep. And I love my sleep! But I bet I get less than five hours a night!?" Newt persisted in looking uncertain as to what to say. "I don't think I am anxious or stressed, but maybe I am. I can tell you," I looked up, "I feel emotionally numb the majority of the time. Not sad. Just numb. Nothing phases me. Nothing interests me. It is the most awful feeling. I can see myself doing it, but I struggle to raise myself out of it. Do you know what I mean?" Newt nodded, though I knew she had never felt that way herself. She just realised any statement would be unhelpful at that moment. I needed support. "I have this face I put on when I am with people. It's a face I have worn for years. The confident and happy face of a contented, determined man. But he's not really there. It's a lie. A deception to get through situations." I paused. "I am rational. I know others need to see that confident guy so that they may provide me with opportunity and purpose. But its draining. I feel like I have been doing it for so long I don't know which face is the real me anymore. Have I fundamentally changed? Can I get the real me back? Christ, it's all fucked up!"

Newt allowed the silence to return. Something had appeared to have resonated inside her and she seemed close to finally structuring her thoughts, although something, maybe her opening statement, who knows, still eluded her. A specific lever to prise the door open towards a more upbeat dialogue. It eventually materialised.

"Are you eating?" She asked. I looked back, puzzled by her question. "You just look like you're losing weight!"

"I don't know. Maybe." I answered a little dismissively, feeling she had missed the point of everything I had just said.

"I only ask because it's one of the signs of depression. Loss of appetite." I ignored her observation, still consumed by my own ponderings. "Have you ever heard of a guy called Maslow?" She continued. "He came up with this structure for looking at what motivates us. It's like a pyramid. As you ascend through the levels you get closer to appreciating your life and yourself." My silence persisted. "It just strikes me it may be worth considering now, because on the bottom layer are the physiological needs. The essentials we all need in our life. Our *rudimentary needs*."

"And this has what to do with weight loss?" I failed to contain my sarcasm.

"Food is one of them." She gave a wry smile. "The lack of appetite is a symptom of depression. It pushes you below the bottom layer."

"Don't start preaching at me, Newt!" I rubbed my face. "Please..."

"Not preaching. Just trying to show how some things can be linked. Despondency leads to apathy, which leads to abstinence. And before you know it, one of the foundation blocks of your needs has gone. That's when feeling depressed can become a self-fulfilling prophecy." She paused. "You have less energy, leading to increased tiredness. Physical weakness undermines mental strength and the spiral continues. I'm not saying pig out and all will be well. But life is a process. Sometimes you just need help to find a good place to start!" She reached out and grasped my forearm, which rested on the tabletop.

"You're using a lot of big words..." I looked towards her. "Be careful you don't go over my head. I'm not exactly at my most astute."

"I doubt I could lose you." She smirked compassionately as her hand slipped from my wrist.

I paused for a moment to consider her comments. "Well, I do eat. Nothing changed there. I'm trying to cut out booze though. Some days are better than others for that..." I gestured towards my pint. She said nothing. "Come on then! I know you're itching to tell me about this pyramid thing. What am I not doing? Where is it going wrong? Why am I failing?"

"It's not like that!" She defended herself. "You can't think about why you are failing. Instead, think about what success is for you and what you can do to achieve it. That's what Maslow's hierarchy is. A simple psychological map for happiness." She smiled. "He suggested there are five levels of human needs. And he proposed that we can only ascend to the next level once everything is in place on the level we are at."

"So, if I'm eating okay, I can get off the bottom rung?" I quipped.

"No." She smirked. "There are six criteria at the base of the pyramid. Six fundamentals we all need in our lives to feel stable." Just then, Tif, another friend, walked into the pub. She picked up a beer mat, tapping its edge on the tabletop, seemingly agitated by his arrival. Continuing at pace, she seemed to want to finish her introduction to Maslow's base layer before Tif joined them. "Food is one of them and water another. Then there's the need for sleep. The need for shelter. The need to have a body that feels like it's working. And, don't laugh, but the need for sex." I laughed anyway.

"Sounds like my kind of conversation!" Tif grinned with pursed lips while nodding. I glanced up at him, reaching my hand out to shake his. "Now there's something I never thought I'd hear a woman say! She needs sex!" He jested.

"Don't you start antagonising her straight away!" I said assertively.

"Yes, women need sex." Newt tapped the beer mat against the tabletop again, revealing her tension. "They may not want it as much or as often as men do, but they definitely need it. I can assure you of that! Maybe we would want it more if men were better at it!?"

"If that's what you think, Newton dear, then you've been getting seen to by the wrong men." Tif asserted cheekily as he sat down.

Tif the Misunderstood

Tif could be considered the odd ball of my 'therapy' group. He was named by his parents after a character in a long-running Belgian comic strip called Tif et Tondu. *These two eponymous cartoon stars resembled better-known characters from their national graphic art competitor,* Tintin.

Tif, the cartoon character, resembled a mid-life Tintin with less hair, which was probably meant ironically, 'tif' being a French colloquialism for 'hair'. Tondu was a shipwrecked sea captain that travelled with him on adventures. Unlike Tintin though, Tif was portrayed in the comics as reckless and a ladies' man. A rounder. A débauché. A libertine. All attributes that for the most part matched my friend to perfection.

Tif, the human, was a high-energy individual. Some would say cocksure. The latter term also inadvertently reflected his approach to life. Six foot tall, with a large, muscular frame, dark brown hair, blue eyes and a face that could charm a snake, he always carried himself with confidence. He wore smart-casual clothes that struck a balance between inconspicuous and noteworthy. His attire always matching its intent—which was to be seen by those he was meeting—projecting a façade of deliberate effort for his companion, whilst also sufficiently restrained to appear unremarkable to all others. He professed there was an art to blending in, that no-strings encounters of a debauchee demanded. Though I could never discern where this began or ended.

For as long as I had known him, Tif had been a womaniser. He loved women in every way possible and was enthusiastic in his pursuit of mutual gratification. More than a pastime, it was a hobby to him. Over the years, he had entertained our boutique friendship group with outlandish tales of his adventures. The richly-perverted stories were never too detailed to dismiss the need for imagination or demonstrate disrespect for his companion, but always sufficiently elaborate to elicit an uncomfortable grimace of disbelief from our cohort. It might be expected that such a friendship was unlikely and I had often thought the same. The only reason I could give for its endurance was that Tif never regaled us as a conqueror of women, but more as an explorer of all things sexually stimulating. Engaging with willing participants in enacting natural desires. Now that may be a challenging concept to decipher, a moral tightrope, but it was the most apt explanation. Tif never presented his experiences as one directional, they were always mutual. He never objectified the woman, they had names, lives that were rich in diversity; that he thrived on knowing and understanding as much as he thrived to delight them physically.

Girlfriends, escorts, swingers, and affairs. Tif had experimented with all. He had often joked that one day he may need to sit back and catalogue each encounter in turn, but wasn't certain how best to do that. Names in the realms within which he had travelled were rarely real. They were pseudonyms. Artificial identities of the people his fellow travellers longed to be. This dark world was void of social conscience. Half-truths were the unwritten subtext and sometimes added an additional spark, when endeavouring to strip back the persona, to reveal the reality beneath. The best lies rarely being completely divorced from real life. More frequently, the truth was just wrapped in an opaque orb to distort it sufficiently and provide the desired anonymity.

So instead of cataloguing his partners by name, he had considered using sexual identifiers instead. Whether his partner had been heterosexual, bisexual, a crossdresser, or transgender. Or even just profile their preferences. Their deviant proclivities. Submissive, dominant, switch, vanilla or bondage-discipline sadomasochism. Or maybe keep it even simpler and profile based on geography or nationality. In the end, he gave up on the idea. Because while the catalogue would have held a diary-like aesthetic to it, he concluded it veered too close to demeaning his partners, both professional and amateur.

From all his exploits, the one tale that he had recounted to the group which lingered in my mind, was of his first real sexual encounter. Not the girl he had lost his virginity to at the age of seventeen. Although that was a hysterical story involving an orchard, a broken condom, a pair of blood-spattered boxers, the grimace of discomfort on his partner's face and the terror of waiting for a phone call the next day to confirm the morning-after pill had been successfully secured and administered. No, the most recalled encounter was of his first girlfriend at university. A nightmare of a relationship that was just deeply, and disturbingly, infused with physicality.

The girl in question had been on Tif's course. She had been slender, five foot seven, had a good figure and long, dark auburn hair. She wasn't a classical beauty, but had one of those faces that held unusual interest. Not ugly, but quirky. For discretion, Tif had dispensed with her name, but to aid my narration, she will be referred to as Miss Psycho or Miss P for reasons that will become evident.

Tif had hooked up with her at the end of the first term. They had been walking back one night from a college event, a foreign exchange students general meeting. Now that may seem dull, but it was far from it. It involved the partaking of excessive quantities of alcohol, including the sampling of liqueurs from foreign lands. At this particular meeting, the foreign beverage had been Aquavit, or Akvavit for the Scandinavians who had brought it. Made from grains and potatoes, Aquavit was presented as a more refined version of the Irish Potcheen, despite being equally intoxicating. It had a kick. And as Tif would discover later, it accelerated impaired judgment and diminished self-control. Literally within an hour of taking a couple of generous measures, he had found himself walking alone with Miss Psycho, back to their halls of residence. In one fleeting moment he still remains unable to explain, he had looked at her and she had looked back, and the next thing he remembered, they were snogging each other's faces off on the pavement and the pursuit of sexual gratification had commenced. Physical frolics had continued immediately afterwards back in her room. Following a semi-uncomfortable exchange of words with her roommate about providing a little space for them to get personal, they'd got down to business. It had been five o'clock in the evening. Two hours or so later, they had emerged to return to the union bar for evening festivities. More alcohol was consumed and the night had ended with a completely ridiculous yet legendary session in one of the rooms adjoining the main television room in the basement of their halls of residence.

Now that may seem harmless. Indeed, it may be considered creative in pursuit of overcoming the obstacle of shared rooms. However, what neither of them had the presence of mind to identify at the time, was the room was not an isolated annex, but formed an integral part of the passageway along the building's basement. To this day, Tif had no idea if anyone had walked past them that night, but he knew by the end of it, they were butt-naked going for a record and Miss P had been a very vocal participant.

It was then the problems had begun. Because their coming together had meant more to her than to him. Significantly more! It had only been three days from the end of term when their antics had started, so Tif had literally ridden it out with a smile on his face. When they headed home for Christmas, he thought time and a little distance would quench the passion swelling in her head. However, shortly after Christmas day, he received a letter from her in the post, expressing how he was the one for her. The one she had been looking for. How she couldn't imagine being without him and how happy he made her. That was when the fun got complicated. Or as an American might say, 'shit got real'. Tif knew he had to break up with her, which he did the first night back at university. But she hadn't received the news well. As emotionally volatile and vocal as she had been in ecstasy, she had taken the drama to new unrequited heights in rejection. And that had just been the start of it.

Her first step, phase one, had been to target their friends and classmates. Brand him as wicked. Tif had let this happen, taking a step back, distancing himself to give her time to heal. But no such healing came and his friends eventually began to see that maybe there was another side to the story. So as he was gradually absorbed back into the club, Miss Psycho's response had been to visit his personal tutor. This was phase two.

A personal tutor is part of the teaching faculty assigned to each student when they arrive at university. They are supposed to be someone who the student can go to for advice and support. A friendly sympathetic face. What Tif discovered is that, when such tutor is advised in extreme detail of his assigned undergraduates consensual antics by a biased third party, they can be prone to falter in their supportive duties. Such faltering was the gift bestowed on Tif by Miss

P's pout-inspired charm, low-cut top, heaving breasts and vivid storytelling. Now it could be suggested that such acts of retribution would have been sufficient to allow closure. And that if reflected on, such endeavours may not be considered the best path to reigniting the Akvavit moment. But like most people trapped in emotional turmoil, rationality was absent, and Miss P's pursuit of him blinkered and relentless.

Phase three was to act out her emotion physically, by threatening to harm herself. Such declarations can never be ignored and should be worked through. So Tif tried to offer compassion, deciding to visit her room one night to talk. He had found her laid on the bed, crying, but when she realised it was him, she immediately sat up and wiped away her tears. He'd sat down on a chair at the foot of the bed and they'd chatted calmly. Sensibly even. Tif explained that there was no going back. That they were finished and had been for some time. And that was when she dropped the next bombshell. Phase four. Would he settle for a physical relationship only? His response to this offer was one of only two things he told us he really regretted about his actions through that relationship. A response that upon reflection briefly exposed his then eighteen-year-old immaturity. Two words that revealed his inner adolescent idiot. 'Prove it'. Instantaneously, she had dropped to her knees and reached out to draw down his trouser zip. That was when Tif's senses had returned. He had lowered his hands with urgency to stop her. Stood up and left saying, 'I can't do this'.

He hadn't forgotten or dismissed her threat of self-harm under phase three though, fearing it might not have run its course, so had gone directly to see one of their classmates in the adjacent hall, and asked him to go sit with her for a while. Make sure she was alright. Ensure she didn't make good on her threat. He had surmised that she had at last moved on when he had seen her the next day in the lecture theatre, happy and smiling, and most importantly, unharmed. He had been wrong. She had just changed tactic again. Phase five was the waiting game.

Three months passed and Tif had met someone new. They'd gone out only once, yet the news had made its way back to Miss P, who chose to confront Tif in the same basement room where six months before they had barely uttered an intelligible word to each other. Her rhetoric was a plea for information to see whether the rumour was true and to which Tif had confirmed the situation. She had started bawling, wailing about how much she still cared. And then, the moment of Tif's second regret arrived. Miss P had proclaimed:

"Well, she is more beautiful than me!", and he had simply replied:

"Yes, she is."

He explained to us that he wasn't proud of his reply, kicking her when she was down, but he'd known that any endeavour to console could have obliterated all the distance he had tried to place between them. He had always remembered her face at that precise moment. It had been one of calm acceptance, of final acknowledgment that all her efforts had been for nothing. But while he read her expression for what it probably was, the moment of serenity was fleeting. Terminated by a shriek of "You bastard!" as she ran out through a fire door.

Nothing more had been said about the matter after that, but it had not been her final gesture. The following Valentine's Day, an envelope arrived in his departmental pigeonhole. Inside, had been a large postcard with a picture of a little boy, sunglasses on, sticking his tongue out and flipping the finger. On the blank reverse side was inscribed the handwritten words, 'To a lost cause. From someone who *is reminded of you by this picture'. He'd shown his friends the card and that was the moment he had been christened with his only university nickname. Misunderstood.*

Despite the years that had passed, in keeping with his university nickname, people still often got the wrong impression about Tif. He wasn't as shallow as his rhetoric could sometimes lead them to believe. Yes, he could be singularly minded. Yes, he had an obsession, an unhealthy and morally eroding addiction for seeking physical pleasure which only required a willing lady with a pulse and a place. Yes, he was a bounder, but one with a conscience. He never acted with disrespect. Self-harm was the only injury from each encounter. Harm that his increasingly detached psyche would begin to normalise the dark desires and make him incapable of real affection. But that was his risk. His burden.

PROPONENT OF THE PHYSIOLOGICAL

"Sex is the answer!" Tif grinned like a hyena. "I'm down with that!"

I mustered a pathetic smile, while Newt shook her head disapprovingly.

"You have a singular mind that I will never understand or appreciate. We are here to support Ethan and all you can do is joke!"

"I'm always here for him! He knows that. I don't need to be serious to be supportive." He gave a playful sneer. "You ever consider that you might be able to learn something from my more jovial approach?"

"Nope! I can honestly say I've never thought that." She sneered back.

"Magnanimous as ever." He quipped. "Alright! Don't let me interrupt this riveting insight into the male psyche." He gestured for her to continue.

"Tell me more about how you feel?" Newt turned to face me.

"That's a tough question to answer, because most of the time I don't feel anything." Tif's forehead furrowed with concern at my opening declaration, but as Newt did, he waited to hear more. "I feel helpless. Like there's nothing I can do to improve things. I know it's not true, but it gets hard to see beyond what feels like repeated rejection."

"Everyone gets down sometimes, mate!" Tif replied.

"If it was only every now and again, I wouldn't be here. But the feeling never subsides. I can see it affecting me in other ways."

"Like?" Tif probed.

"I don't know! It's hard to explain, really." I thought about it briefly. "It's the small things, I guess. A lack of energy and with that a lack of interest in everything."

"Like?" Tif persisted.

"Like watching television. I just don't care what's on. It could be anything. Memory muscle just makes my eyes stare at the screen, but there's no interest." I sighed. "Some days when I am at home on my own, a sense of tiredness will take over. I know I am not actually tired. I know it's an unnatural apathy, but I find myself laying on the floor anyway, resting my hands on my chest and closing my eyes."

"What do you think about?" Newt asked.

"Nothing and everything. Everything that hasn't gone right for me, through to the emptiness of my future."

"Your future's not empty!" Tif objected.

"Maybe, but I don't know what's in it."

"No one does." Newt calmly stated. "I know it can seem hard, but you need to find a way forward. I'm not going to tell you to wake up and shake yourself down. But you do need to find something to hold on to."

"I agree!" Tif uncharacteristically offered Newt support and not sarcasm.

The three of us fell silent for a moment. I looked down at the table in thought. Tif and Newt briefly glanced at each other, as if waiting and wondering what to do next. Then they looked over at the barman, who was staring at us in puzzlement.

Despite Newt admonishing his light-hearted approach to issues, Tif was capable of being serious; and in that seriousness, sometimes offer valid constructive comment. This was one of those times.

"Can you remember when we got that summer job working in that potash mine up north?" I nodded. Newt shook her head no. "The mine was the deepest in the country. The shafts were twelve hundred metres straight down. It took five minutes to ride the cage to the bottom and when we got there, they had those transit vans with the backs cut out and benches welded to the chasse for seating, that drove us out to the production areas. It was crazy!" I stayed silent and Newt waited for Tif to continue. "The mine was kind of on two levels. The main roadways for material, men and ventilation were cut through a bed of salt that laid underneath the potash. The salt bed was stronger and held its shape. Then every hundred metres or so, they would dig a roadway up into the potash above. Establishing six parallel production headings, they mined the potash with what could only be described as a fail-safe system. You remember that?" He asked as if to make sure I was listening. I nodded.

"What do you mean *'fail-safe'*? We're not all miners after all!" Newt reminded him.

"What I mean is they had these thin pillars in between the six production headings. The pillars were designed to fail slowly, releasing stress from the surrounding rock. As the headings advanced, the pillars would fracture and crumble. There were no steel arches either. All they used to reinforce the roof and walls were rock-bolts." Newt looked puzzled again. "Imagine you have a hundred sheets of paper. It's quite loose. Could easily fall apart. Well, if you got six bolts and pushed them perpendicular through the sheets, then on the end of each put a washer and nut, and tightened, the paper would stop acting like one hundred separate sheets, but like one thicker sheet. That's what rock-bolts do, just with rocks." Newt nodded in understanding. "Now think of those blocks of paper. Two standing upright and one spanning the gap. As you push down on the top, the horizontal pack would feel quite stiff, but the vertical packs would bulge between the bolts as the leaves bent out. That's kind of what happens in the rock. The top remains a solid beam, but the supports bend and break. Spalling until you are able to put your arm right through the pillar." He stretched his arm out like a Parisian mime artist imagining the pillar. "Freaky, really." He retracted his arm. "You remember that?" He looked over at me again.

"I mostly remember how hot it was. And the refrigerated cabins we sat in at break times."

"Oh yes! That was weird." He paused in thought for a moment. "Anyway, the point of all this explanation is that I was working in one of the production headings, charging up a blast pattern one day. When suddenly there was this deafening crash behind me, as part of the pillars finally gave up and let a huge section of the bolted roof smash down. The heading filled with tiny particles of salt and potash dust, burning my nose and eyes, and enflaming the scratches and scars on my hands and forearms. I couldn't see anything. Not even my hands. My headlamp illuminated the air like a car's headlights in the fog. The light reflected straight back like I was wrapped in a dense white blanket. I panicked big time. Then the voice of my supervisor sounded out. 'Tif, don't worry. If you hear it, you're alive!'" He paused. "Maybe not the most reassuring words that could have been spoken, but they were instantly calming with their irrefutable logic. Of course that only works for a moment, cause then you start wondering whether another slab might drop." He let out a contained laugh.

"Is that it?" Newt questioned. "You know, you could have just said 'what doesn't kill you makes you stronger'!" She smiled.

"Yes, but then you would have missed the subtle messaging in my story!" Tif grinned back.

"Which is?" She asked.

"Just like in mining, with life, you never know what's in front of you and it doesn't matter what's behind you. Once it's happened, there's nothing that can be undone!" A smug grin erupted wide across his face.

"Very good. But I think you could have stuck with a punchier analogy!"

"Consider yourself lucky." Tif replied. "I nearly went with my Phantom Crapper story, finishing with the strapline 'shit happens'!" Even I smiled a little this time.

The Phantom Crapper was a classic tale of boarding-school Britain. Tif and I had attended a private school in Nottinghamshire. It was a picture postcard school sat on the outskirts of an industrial northern town. Three hundred years old, four stories high, red brick construction with turrets and towers, it heralded the prestige it offered. Sprawling lawns and playing fields surrounded it, framing through the vast campus space, the opulence and privilege of the student body. But as with all congregations of entitled youth, the behaviour frequently failed to match the prestige branding bestowed upon them, and the Phantom Crapper was one example.

It had all began one morning when Tif and I had been in sixth form. The bell had sounded for the start of the day and the silent ritual of pre-breakfast dressage had begun. But the quiet beautification hadn't survived long. On a shared landing area between two schoolhouses, communal toilets and bathrooms lined one side. In one of these toilets, someone, during the night, had failed deliberately to unload their excrement into the bowl. Instead depositing it like a curled, but significantly sized snail, atop the cistern. The morning titillation from the students at the discovery had been equally countered by the fury of the faculty. Every student from both houses had been called before their respective housemasters and demands levelled for the culprit to reveal themself, else suffer more stringent punishment if they had to be unearthed. Yet nobody took claim for the act and school life steadily returned to normality in absence of closure. A week passed and the faculty fury had calmed down too, assuming the collective threat had served its purpose.

On the eighth morning after the first discovery, they struck again. Bolder this time around. Not content with the closed-door privacy of a toilet cubicle, they laid their waste on the flagstone stairs that led to the first floor, which happened once again to be the communal area between the same two schoolhouses. But rather than lay the blame for a second time between these two groups, the faculty took greater exception to this follow-on act of contempt, escalating the issue to encompass the entire studentship, the pupil collective being briefed and accused at morning assembly. This time, threats of ever-increasing severity were levelled by the headmaster. The myth had been publicly validated and made legend. And like a Marvel superhero, the Phantom Crapper was born.

As with all legends, time gilded the daring endeavours of the Phantom. Chinese whispers swelled the magnitude of the deposits and embellished the circumstances of their discovery. Kids began to lay claim to hearing noises on the landing and stairwell the nights of the first two forays into defecating freedom. The buzz around school was palpable, as everyone waited to see if they would strike again. They did. This time waiting two weeks before the clandestine baring of their arse. Ego evidently swelling the Phantom's bravery, this third and final venture led them to the central cloisters of the ground floor and the ejection of waste at the foot of the teachers' common room door. It was only in a world pre-CCTV and smartphones that such brazen act could be successfully undertaken. Nothing laid a trail to the legend's door. No clues and no tell-tales offered insight. After all the faculty threats of retribution, they found themselves outplayed. They couldn't discipline three hundred and fifty students for the act of a sole individual or small group that couldn't be identified. Nevertheless, more hollow disciplinary assertions followed, but they fell on sceptical ears.

That said, the Phantom never struck again. Why would they? The legend had been created. The teachers outwitted. Short of breaking into the headmaster's house and dropping a load on his study desk, there was no way to better their success.

Newt hadn't heard the story before, but the eponymous title kind of surrendered the eloquence of the anecdote; so she declined to enquire further.

"Anyway!" She cut short the reminiscence of older years. "On a more objective footing, if I can continue where I was a minute ago.

Maslow had two layers at the base of his triangle of needs. These layers being the physiological needs which I've already mentioned, and the safety needs. These are the physical, health, emotional and financial security needs." Newt explained.

"I'm a proponent of the physiological needs!" Tif announced.

Newt replied. "I don't think we need to be reminded of that."

"All I'm saying is, who really needs to feel safe? Tomorrow is a question mark for all of us. So why not just live in the moment? Why not embrace what's in front of you." Tif offered justification.

"Because this leads to a selfish life of shallow experiences absent of emotional growth!" She retorted, sounding like a textbook extract.

"All I'm suggesting is that sometimes it's worrying about tomorrow that brings you down!" Tif defended himself.

"And all I'm saying is that with emotional growth, you can't ignore tomorrow." Her voice softened. "As we build relationships, we live for others as well as for ourselves. We have a responsibility to them to have an idea of tomorrow. We can't be kids forever!" Turning away from Tif, she asked me, "Don't you agree, Ethan?"

I took the remark as an attempt to reengage with my distress. "Yes, I worry about tomorrow. Worry about what I will become." I responded.

"And look where it's getting you!" Tif interrupted.

"I feel like I'm caught in a loop. I worry about tomorrow, while at the same time reliving days that have passed. All the time, failing to embrace today. This moment! So maybe there is something to be said for your promiscuity." I conceded. Though my words were uttered at best in ambivalent endorsement of Tif's approach because I knew he was also failing to live for now. To seize the opportunities in the moment. Because he was trapped in a battle between worry and bitterness of his own making.

"Don't start giving in to him, Ethan! You know he has no shame and feels no guilt." Newt reached to hold my hand. "You do though! You think you feel down now. Just see how things feel if you lay guilt over everything."

"I'm not being deliberately difficult here, dear!" Tif always used the term *dear* when he was annoyed. "Two things: if you live in the moment, you don't feel guilt. What's past is passed." He grinned. "Secondly, don't knock it till you've tried it!"

"I don't think so!" She dismissed his prose. "I don't need to undermine my beliefs to know I would feel guilt."

"Then that's the shackles you chose to wear, *dear*." Tif challenged.

"And I wear them willingly because they are worn out of love and respect for those I care about!" Newt threw the ball back into his corner.

"Okay. Let me give you an illustration of living in the moment."

"I'm not sure we can take another one of your stories just yet..." Newt shut him down gently.

"Hey! We're all here to help Ethan, so let's try and keep an open mind to each other's point of view, okay?" Newt remained mute to his smirk. "Right, so I was down in Cardiff working, staying in a hotel just outside the city centre. It was shortly after all the regeneration work, so the area had a new feel to it."

"It's a nice place, Cardiff. Been there myself for work..." I commented.

"Definitely! Anyway, it was during my days of paying for fun. I'd arranged a meeting with this young Welsh lass. I can't remember exactly, but she was around nineteen. Skinny. Pretty attractive. I'm digressing a little though! So, she turned up at my door with a friend. Another girl." He looked at Newt. "Before you suggest anything, no, I had only booked the one girl."

"The thought never crossed my mind." She smirked.

"Well, I didn't know what to say. My expected date explained her friend was just starting out in the profession and needed some practice. She could either just sit and watch or join in, that was up to me. No additional charges either way."

"I bet you loved that." Newt made her disgust clear.

"That's my point! I didn't live completely in the moment. I worried about whether it was a ruse to rob me. So I said no. Made her friend wait in the hotel lobby." Tif explained.

"So what is your point? Don't look a gift horse in the mouth?" She quipped.

"Not really. Probably more like 'seize the day'. Carpe diem."

Newt shook her head. "I really do worry about you sometimes. I worry about your choices and your influence on our friends!" She gestured toward me. "Friends who need more than a moment's elation to find their feet again."

The disappointment in Newt's tone was obvious. She kept attempting to maintain a sensible dialogue that offered a way forward, but Tif persisted in interrupting with his anecdotal nonsense. All it served was to distract from real progress.

A Lustful Downfall

I had considered, as I knew Newt hoped, that once Tif had accepted the morally low ground promiscuity proliferated, he would avert from his path of immorality. But Tif firmly believed the body was there to be used and savoured. Such beliefs overpowered any guilt. While he would ultimately acknowledge the moral complexity and risks from his sexual liaisons, the ultimate carnal objective from them remained as tantalising to him as it had ever been. So his solution to feed the hunger had been forced to evolve in unison with the understanding of his motivations.

"Anyway, I've been through the paid-for service avenue more times than I care to remember, you know!" Tif announced, seeming unashamed of the moral unacceptability of his declaration. "And I know it isn't a destination I'll chose to revisit again!"

"Why?" Newt questioned. "I thought it'd be perfect for you! Detached. Functional."

"And you'd be wrong! It's not the money side of it either. It's the inconsistency." Tif declared. I looked around and felt reassured to see equal bemusement on Newt's face. "Several encounters have been very pleasurable, but the vast majority have been empty. Void of credible emotion. Believe me, the fictional whimpering of ecstasy is readily distinguishable from genuine elation!" He seemed to pause for a moment's reflection. "In fact, from all my encounters, I can probably say with some certainty that only during three of them did something genuine occur."

"By 'genuine', what do you mean exactly?" I queried.

"I mean the sense of something approximating an unremunerated passionate encounter." Nobody spoke, so Tif continued. "Let me elaborate. The first encounter was with a young lady of middle eastern origins. She spent much longer with me than she was booked for and even forgot to ask for payment afterwards. I was the one who reminded her as I escorted her out of the hotel."

"Are you trying to declare that your love-making performances are so good you can sweep any hooker off their feet?" Newt remarked and we both laughed.

"No!" Tif responded sharply. "Anyway, the second lady was much older. Again, spent longer with me than she was supposed to, and afterwards blanketly refused any payment because she had enjoyed herself so much."

"You're just bragging now!" I quipped.

"I'm not! But there is more to sex than vanilla exploits, you know!" Tif retorted flippantly. "The third was a young British lady. She had taken her payment upfront, but remained afterwards to have a drink and a chat without any additional financial incentive. During that conversation we agreed upon a proposal for free sex. If I agreed to make my hotel room available to her to host in-calls whenever I was in town, then she would repay in physical kind." Everyone looked stunned. "I'll admit it was a weird relationship but it lasted over a year. And it was a very good year!"

"Okay, so you're good in the sack and a good negotiator." Newt concluded. "I am still not sure why you're telling us all this!?"

"Just sharing some wisdom. Because for the rest of the escorts I have met, there have been scant moments when the mainly emotionally vacuous encounters have been okay, and so many more mis-marketed encounters where the profile picture and description proved undeniably disingenuous." Tif juddered at his thoughts. "Where a size twelve was actually size sixteen plus. Where 'considered good looking for my age' meant the youthful pre-pregnancy moist skin was a distant memory. Where clean apartment translated to mean a squalid hovel with a single dimly-lit and darkly-decorated bedroom, with a solitary double bed adorned in dowdy, crinkled sheets, topped by a fresh bath towel to hide the markings of previous punters and provide a clean surface on which to lay."

"Oh, you do paint a beautiful picture..." Newt announced with an appalled tone.

"Yep, those desperate service providers relied completely on the generosity, lust or politeness of their customers to accept their real form." Tif observed.

"Did it ever stop you saying yes though?" Newt cynically remarked.

"Yes actually!" Tif grinned. "Every time! Irrespective of how much they hurled abuse!" Then his face scrunched up as if he'd recalled something distasteful. "Well, nearly every time. There was this one time my instincts failed me..."

"Please elaborate." Newt encouraged, although she sounded disingenuous. Her voice apathetic, as if she knew there was no alternative but to listen to the story anyway.

"The venue was in a quaint little Yorkshire village. The woman had asked me to park at the local pub called the Spread Eagle. How appropriate, right?" He paused, expecting a reaction from us, but we remained silent. "Anyway, I walked up to her house, which was pretty large, probably with four bedrooms, more suited in scale for a brothel than an independent escort's shag pad I would say. I remember the outside showed slight signs of age, but the thing that caught my eye was the bottom right-hand corner of the front door, which had been kicked through. I should have suspected something then but for whatever reason I didn't."

"Maybe your sixth sense was preoccupied with lustful thoughts?" Newt quipped. "Or was little Tif leading the charge?"

Tif ignored her. "When she opened the door, she vaguely resembled her pictures. Ushering me inside, she led me upstairs. At the top, a young boy had appeared from a door on the right. Wearing just a t-shirt and a pair of pants. He looked about three years old. The woman had taken him by the hand and led him back into the room he'd emerged from, directing me to go the other direction and enter the first room on the left. A couple of minutes elapsed before she caught up. From the moment she entered the bedroom it felt like 'escorting by numbers', like she was on an activity schedule. She went through the motions, transferring from one action to another as if they were set pieces of a play. No subtle fluidity. No attention to detail." He took a breath. "No passion! Her hands moved with callous precision. It was a fantasy girlfriend experience, choreographed under the clumsy stage direction of *taking one for the team*. I had considered leaving before we had even got to the bed!"

"So why didn't you?" Newt asked.

"Already paid her. And while I'm not proud of it, think I'd resigned myself to receiving some value for that."

"That's sad, mate." I contributed.

"I know! But we live and learn. Anyway, as she'd begun to pull my boxers off, the bedroom door opened and the young boy from the landing walked straight in. I was surprised, but didn't flinch. Just laid there, unashamed, in my full glory."

"You do realise how bad that sounds?" Newt sounded increasingly ashamed of her friend.

"Yes, definitely not one of my proudest moments!" He raised his eyebrows, seeming to concede to the criticism. "Well, the woman immediately dismounted and slipped on a dressing gown, all the while shouting at the kid to leave, before dragging him out and back down the corridor. I waited a few more minutes and when she returned, she asked if I could go and wait in my car while she sorted the boy out. She assured me that she would call when everything was okay to return. And that was when the penny dropped. The whole event had been staged. A desperate person's hustle. Never been so angry at myself."

"So did you take her to task?" I asked.

"Hell no! She was tiny and had a kid. I figured she wouldn't do something like this without backup on hand. A big burly brute who went to the gym three times a day and could lift me up with one hand. So as uncharacteristic as it may seem for me to shy away from conflict, I conceded to a disservice and left. Chalked the event up to experience."

"Some people will never learn..." Newt remarked sarcastically.

"Not so, my dear! The whole encounter proved to be my final foray into lustful satisfaction through the surgical hands of a financial transaction." Tif smirked. "It crystalised what I wanted from my escapades."

"What was that?" I enquired.

"Something more. Something genuinely tactile and sensual." Tif clarified.

"How did that work out for you then?" Newt interjected.

"Pretty good actually! That was when I discovered swinging." Tif spoke with enthusiasm.

"Honestly! Are there no depths to which you won't sink?" Newt's disappointment persisted.

"Like I said before. Don't knock it till you've tried it, dear! It's a logical solution to sexual frustrations. It just requires a little perseverance!"

"Thought you could have just gone to one of those clubs?" I questioned.

"Yes I could have, but I kind of viewed those as only slightly removed from the functionality of escorts!" Tif justified his choices.

"So what approach to swinging do you advocate?"

"Please don't encourage him!" Newt sounded desperate in her attempt to stop the conversation.

"The man wants to know details, my dear!" Tif smirked. "Who am I to refuse him on his journey to discovery?"

Newt resigned to Tif's continued tell-all.

"So, the practice of swinging. 'The scene', as it is frequently referred to." He announced exuberantly. "The world where consenting adults agree to share each other respectfully and freely. You've got singles and couples alike, all satisfying their deviances. People just seeking social interaction mixed with consensual pleasure. It is actually quite liberating. Being absent of follow-on commitment somehow gives a degree of freedom that can deliver fantasies to quell even the most perverse of hungers. But you've got to find a way in first. So here is my guide to new participants into 'the scene'." He emphasised the final two words, casting a quick, brash glance at Newt. "Issue one, identifying swingers." He paused for effect. "On top of the list, and the one most widely acknowledged, is the presence of pampas grass in the garden. Though if you're seeking discrete encounters, such blazoned publicity may not be the best course of action for you. There are other more subtle garden-based indicators available, like the use of white landscaping rocks and pink or purple plants in the front garden, or the excessive presence of garden gnomes. Though the gnomes may also prove troublesome if you have young children who adore garden gnomes. I'm sure garden decorations inspired by *Gnomeo and Juliet* and *Sherlock Gnomes* have been the cause for a few close shaves!"

"So none of those are really practical then?" Newt sounded like she was chiding him.

"Let me continue!" Tif shut her down. "The presence of a hot tub is also considered a serious sign of sexual promiscuity. Again, that could prove unfortunate for those who grew up watching *The Fall Guy* and have always hankered for an outside bath!"

"Not the smartest bunch, these swingers, are they?" She jibed, looking towards me, but Tif ignored her once again.

"Then, on a more personal level, jewellery can be worn to indicate the wearer is sexually relaxed. Things like wearing a black ring on the right hand or displaying an anklet or toe ring, or thumb ring for that matter, or, a little more explicitly, switching a wedding band to the right hand." He waited a couple of seconds for Newt to pass a remark, but she didn't.

"Then going back to home-based decorations, there is the use of a pineapple-shaped door knocker or, alternatively, the display of a can of Mr Sheen in the front window."

"Does any of this actually work?" I asked. "It's not like anyone can simply go cruising around the neighbourhood in search of pampas grass or peak over fences into back gardens looking for steaming hot tubs! And even if they have the signs, you can't casually walk up to a house and ask if they fancy a bit of slap and tickle!"

"Well said, Ethan!" Newt congratulated me, misinterpreting my query as a challenge when it was really intended as a prompt for further useful disclosures.

Tif understood what I was seeking, though, and continued. "In a similar vein, you could say that with the exception of switching wedding bands to the right hand, jewellery is first and foremost a fashion accessory. So while it has some potential as a humorous ice-breaker line in a bar, it can also be problematic in that it concedes everything to the jewellery-wearing recipient to respond as they feel appropriate. Such responses can range from disgust at the mere suggestion of having meaningless sex with a stranger through to disgust that you have had the audacity to deem yourself worthy of a chance. After all, even the promiscuous have standards!"

"Are you speaking from experience?" Newt remarked.

"Not at all! Always been pretty successful if you want to know." Tif resonated with pride.

"So what was your approach?" I urged him to carry on with his guidance.

"Well, being a family man, growing my own pampas grass isn't an option. Not that my wife would notice. Neither is attending swinging clubs, where anonymity is relinquished immediately upon entry by the surrender of a passport or driving licence."

"Thought they were too emotionally cold for you anyway!?" Newt jested mockingly.

"They are, dear, but this is my guidance for Ethan over there! I am just making sure I cover all the facts." Tif sneered at her. "So I did what everybody does these days when they can't find something. I went on the internet. It became rapidly apparent that I wasn't the only one who had decided to resort to exploration of the virtual world to identify and build rapport with like-minded individuals." He took a deep breath. "I tried a few different apps and websites before finally stumbling on *Swing2us*, which purported to have tens of thousands of members."

"All fake I bet!" Newt suggested.

"Just there to get you hooked and take your money?" I quizzed.

"You're both right, but that doesn't mean there weren't people to be found. Although I will confess that I thought I would discover a few quicker than I did. The reality, as you both alluded to, was a web of escorts vying for business, fake accounts attempting to tease me towards registering on different websites, picture collectors who lacked the gumption to live the life they courted, the genuine but unreliable, the genuine but selective, the genuine but unappealing, and the genuine committed and respectful, or *GCR*, as I coined them."

"Cute." Newt smirked condescendingly.

"Finding someone is a time-consuming minefield that demands continuous engagement to weed out the undesirable and allow you to hold on tight to contact with the elusive *GCR*s. Once identified, female and couple *GCR*s always seem to be inundated with approaches. So it is critical to answer as expediently as possible and with words that eclipse the normative but are readily understood by the majority, and yet convey an air of mystery that invites further dialogue."

"You could have just said to be clever and eloquent!" Newt commented. "No need to be so verbose!"

"Some days," Tif paused, "it can feel like an impossible task. Then on others, the perfect words might drip like honey from your tongue to your fingertips as you tap your smartphone. Words that might forge jealousy from the most seasoned marketing professional."

"You're doing the verbose thing again." Newt reminded him.

"Simply trying to give as much guidance as possible! Quality and quantity." He smiled charmingly.

"So how did it work out for you?" I asked.

"Well, my entry into the world of swinging wasn't as rapid as I had hoped, but I eventually managed to inspire a couple of female GCRs to leave the website and explore the narrative, first through email, then on the phone. Both women were similar and yet so different to each other. While physically both were a dress size six to eight."

"Typical!" Newt remarked, I assumed in response to Tif's immediate gravitation toward describing physical form.

Tif carried on. "Both had long brown hair and were around five foot four. Their personalities were poles apart. The first lady was really young. She wore glasses and had a permanently timid and confused expression which revealed her inexperience. Lucinda was in her final year of study at college, training to be a social worker, which seemed odd in juxtaposition to her confessed desires. She had stated on her profile she wanted to be 'someone's submissive on a full-time basis'. She wanted to be constantly instructed and controlled, told who she could see, what she could eat and to be treated as an on-command plaything. Not what I would normally have expected from a social worker, but I guess it takes all sorts!" Tif observed. "I have to be honest, she was a very tantalising proposition, and she was only 22! I could have been her dad for fuck's sake!" He almost looked gleeful.

"That's disgraceful!" Newt admonished.

"Which bit?" Tif grinned.

"All of it! Her age. Your interest. The whole idea of it!" Newt clarified the full extent of her distaste.

"Look, I wasn't making her do it. It was her choice! I didn't objectify her, she did that to herself. I simply grasped the opportunity with both hands for the sake of an experience! And as for age, it's just a number, dear!"

He gave Newt a sharp stare, expecting a comeback. She said nothing.

"Anyway, as I was going to say, we first met for a coffee to explore her hopes for the proposed relationship. Like the consummate interviewer, I questioned and probed her thoughts. She was adorable in her naivety. She'd only ever had sex once before and that encounter had been less than memorable. She told me she'd attended this party, where she'd ended up sleeping with her best friend's ex-boyfriend. The way she recounted the event was cold and emotionless, as if she had simply taken the opportunity to engage in the activity scientifically to understand what the fuss was about and, in so doing, break the stigma around virginity."

"That's awful!" Newt expressed sympathy with Lucinda's questionable decision.

"We all have to start somewhere I guess…" I argued with a pragmatic tone.

"I left that first social meeting wondering how Lucinda could elect to surrender her body and free will to anyone, let alone a complete stranger like me, especially when her only experience to date had yielded such negative sentiments."

"Careful there, Tif. You sound like you might have empathised with her. Surely you wouldn't want to break your distinctive sociopathic character?" Her words were laced with irony.

"Despite this exterior," he gestured to present himself, "I do have compassion for those around me!" He actually seemed offended by Newt's slur. "She was a confused girl in a woman's body, anyone could see that. Even me. Whether her desire to be broken in rather than seduced affectionately was a good one, who am I to judge? And the opportunity in front of me considered objectively in the absence of emotion, like a good sociopath." He sneered at Newt. "I couldn't resist and told her that. So we arranged our first foray into degradation."

"You really can be disgusting, you know!" Newt was increasingly expressing her disdain for Tif's lifestyle and the direction of the conversation.

"We met a week later at a hotel. We met in the bar to settle any nerves. She accepted the drink, but declined the food. The conversation was stilted, mostly led by me. Not surprisingly, she looked exceptionally nervous, like a person preparing to do something they had never considered possible, like a parachute jump, where all was surrendered to fate and the hands of whoever had packed the parachute. I knew she wasn't at risk. But she didn't. She was just a waif, offering herself to be restrained, shackled by a stranger twice her physicality, whom she had spent only ninety minutes of her life with. At least when you jump from a plane the danger is clear and present. In this situation, there were an infinite number of risks that could be levelled upon her by someone without integrity and an appetite for non-consensual abuse. I knew that wasn't me. In the bar though, she was oblivious to my true nature. Her agitation was so evident that, combined with the age gap, we were drawing much attention and speculation from nearby tables. I had to get her out of there and upstairs to the room."

"Oh, how chivalrous of you!" Newt wisecracked.

"We took the lift up in silence. I scanned the key card and unlocked the room door, holding it open for her to lead in and she did, without hesitation. Once inside, I wasted no time, passing her a gift box I'd pulled together containing the clothes I wanted her to wear. Again, without hesitation or comment, she took the package and went straight to the bathroom to get changed."

"Do we really need to hear more?" Newt queried.

"Probably not. Suffice to say it was an intriguing evening!" He grinned. "A step into the unknown for both of us. I felt such power from her relinquishing complete control to me. But then I felt the weight of responsibility that came with it."

"You instantaneously grew a conscience?" Newt remarked snidely. "Wonders will never cease!"

"Dear, contrary to your low opinion of me, I do have one!" Tif replied. "So despite the objective of the encounter being for me to yield my will over her, I discovered myself incapable when there is no intimacy. I realised again how important that was to me. Not sure why this was such a revelation, given why I'd given up on escorts!"

"Maybe it's because you mistakenly view the pinnacle of intimacy to be penetration!?" Newt snapped back. "When, in reality, true intimacy is more mutual, best experienced through a kiss. The way the lips touch lightly, delicate in their offering. Tongue tips savouring each other, feeling the microscopic undulations of taste buds that cover the anterior surface. Sensing the moist internal chasm in stark contrast to the initially dry lips. Then as confidence and appetite grows, lips press harder and tongues delve deeper. Exploring. Stimulating. All the while, eyes locked in mutual gaze centimetres apart. That is when intimacy cannot be faked."

"And you call me verbose!" Tif jested. "I thought you were going to explode!"

"You know me. Ever the passionate one." Newt replied.

"I can't say I've ever seen that side to you!" Tif remarked.

"At least I'm honest with my love!" Newt challenged Tif. "When you are locked in a kiss, you can see straight into the other person's eyes, and eyes are the greatest storytellers. Open portals to the soul. You know, there are forty-three muscles in the face that we use to express ourselves. Around the eyes there are just seven, but this septet is, for the most part, transparent in their portrayal of emotions. They are unable to conceal the owner's true thoughts buried beneath in absence of the other thirty-six."

"Now I think that's true." Tif uncharacteristically agreed with Newt. "Because when I pulled her towards me that first time to kiss her, I saw a complete absence of emotion. No affection. No contempt. No fear. Her eyes were just hollow. And before I'd even started, I realised how out of her depth she was. And how responsible I was for her."

"Back to being like her dad!" I stated.

"Don't say that! The thought makes me cringe." Tif confessed. "I was someone I didn't expect that night. I was kinder. Treated her with kid's gloves. Tried to give her a second sexual encounter that generated positive memories. That drew her emotions to the surface. I don't know if I have been successful. Lucinda's vacant expression or *resting bitch face*, as she called it, disguised all. Afterwards though, she curled up beside me in bed and wrapped her arm tightly around me. So, I guess I must have done alright?"

"Paternal sensations aside, I bet you saw her again." Newt challenged.

"Actually no. In the morning, I'd explained that I felt she needed to experience affection, not submission. Told her she needed to grow in intimacy, before experimenting. And that taking a shortcut to subservience wasn't a solution for avoiding emotion. Emotions were the spark that fires the senses and enhances the stimulation of surrender. Said she needed to know what her body enjoyed, before pushing it to alternative limits."

"Very admirable..." Newt complimented. "For once."

"She actually agreed. Although she did clarify that she still wanted the journey to threshold testing to be a quick one. Which I accepted before walking her to the station with every intention of seeing her again. But I couldn't. I wasn't able to let go of the caring." He took a long

69

slow breath. "I knew she was a prize that many from the swinging scene would use, abuse and discard; and she would have been no better for it. But I just couldn't bring myself to be a link in that chain of degradation, no matter how goodwilled I told myself my intentions were."

"How did she take it?" I questioned.

"I simply explained how I felt in a sequence of emails and advised her to leave the website and focus on finding herself a real partner. She said she was disappointed, but she knew what she wanted."

"Did you keep in touch?" I asked, curious to understand how deep Tif's emotional attachment had been.

"I have! A little like a surrogate dad, I guess. She eventually met someone more normal."

"More normal than you!" Newt exclaimed. "Can't have been too hard."

Tif dismissively shook his head. "She messaged me one day to ask my advice about her boyfriend's ultimatum to engage in a threesome or they would be finished. I suggested that any request like that failed to have consideration for her at its heart and an end was inevitable. So she may as well cut her losses and move on without compromising herself further. She took my guidance and a couple of months later met someone else."

"Good for her." I gave a feeble smile. "And I guess well done to you."

"Maybe you are emotionally maturing at last." Newt offered.

"Maybe. The experience definitely gave me a fresh perspective. I discovered I had limitations. It also clarified that while I need intimacy from my encounters, I need a clear marker for separation of these relationships from my day-to-day life. It needs to be less complicated. Which brings me to lady number two."

"Are we just going to work through your catalogue of escapades tonight?" Newt groaned.

Tif let the words wash over him and ploughed on with his story.

"Joanne was four years older than me, so more age appropriate. In many ways, she could be described as a fifty-year-old version of Lucinda. She had never been married, seeing the formal attachment as an unrequired tether. She lived alone and worked four days a week as a hairdresser. She was very house proud. And as for her body, she was slim and pretty sublimely shaped. I have to say, with due respect to her, she was fantastically preserved for a woman of her years! Although her preservation was probably aided by the absence of the rigours of childbirth and parenting."

"I could say so many things to that, but I'm not going to." Newt was evidently appalled. I looked at her sympathetically while Tif just carried on, completely undeterred.

"Unlike Lucinda, Joanne was tactile and her eyes radiated passion. She wasn't timid by any stretch of the definition. Armoured from a life of self-sufficiency, her confidence exuded every inch of her body and was revealed through the discrete flash of her stocking tops in Starbucks early during our first meeting. I had dared her to wear them and she had risen willingly to the challenge. She also made it clear while we were drinking that it was going to be a relationship of action. Which she subsequently reinforced by passing me her address as she stood up to leave, offering her invitation with the words, 'See you in fifteen minutes'."

"At least there was no ambiguity!" I suggested.

"That's for sure! Anyway, her home was a small terrace house on the outskirts of Sheffield. One bedroom, with an open-plan kitchen and dining area at the rear, and a sitting room at the front, the two areas separated from each other by an enclosed staircase that ascended across the breadth of the building. Upstairs provided a master bedroom to the front of the property, with the main bathroom and a small box room at the rear." For a moment Tif looked as though he was struggling to recall events. "Despite her clear enthusiasm, she offered me another coffee. I courteously accepted of course, but it never got made. To spare Newt's blushes again I will not venture further into the intricacies of the encounter."

"Small mercies." Newt quipped.

"I will however say that the kitchen preceded the dining room table, which preceded the two-seater sofa, which preceded the four-poster bed, which preceded the bedroom floor. Sweat dripped. Time was stolen. And flesh was devoured." He beamed.

"And you just can't help yourself!" Newt sighed.

"It was everything my encounter with Lucinda had failed to be. It was the ultimate embodiment of symbiotic passion."

"More like lust!" She interjected.

"Not at all! Our bodies instinctively knew the perfect reaction to each other's action. We managed to keep the physical evolution escalating to the point at which all our energy was spent! It was divine."

"Are you still seeing her?" I enquired.

"No. We did meet a few more times though. She craved more and was prepared to surrender herself in the process. Compared to Lucinda, I took full advantage of that control." He smiled.

"And you're proud of yourself for that?" Newt questioned.

"Kind of. There were no strings. No need to arrange accommodation. No deceit. Just unadulterated pleasure on tap." Tif replied.

"So why stop seeing her?" I asked.

"Because, unfortunately, as time advanced, Joanne's contentment to continue as the other woman diminished. She tired of my unreliable availability resulting from my real life. While both of us declared that our encounters were fantastic, the elation eventually failed to be countered by the cumulative disappointment of my last-minute cancellations. So, inevitably, what was a utopian situation abruptly ended in a short exchange of assertive texts."

An Addiction

"What did you expect? There is no such thing as no-strings passion!" Newt commented.

"You can say what you want. While I may have mourned the loss of that sexual paragon, I also affirmed that the 'scene' was the answer to my lasting problem of carnal pacification. A way for me to balance my sanity."

"May work for you, but I think you are misguided in considering it the right solution for everyone." Newt remarked, gesturing her head towards me, before staring back at Tif. "You know you're an addict, don't you?" She accused.

"I don't see myself that way." Tif retorted. "It's my choice to do something I enjoy. Some people exercise, I like engaging in sex."

"That's what you tell yourself, I'm sure. But every addict finds ways to justify their habit. But it's still an addiction."

"Bollocks!" Tif dismissed her.

"Very defensive there!" She challenged.

"What? Just because I don't accept everything you say I'm defensive?" Tif was clearly riled by her persistent judgement.

"I'll prove it to you, if you like!" Newt instigated her process of persuasion with a more passive tone.

"Here we go..."

Tif remained guarded. I guessed he thought it was a no-win scenario. Agree to the scrutiny and Newt would find a way to confirm her accusation. Decline, appear dismissive and be considered to prove her point by default without debate. He sighed reluctantly.

"Okay. Let's go."

"Do you know what addiction is?" She asked.

"Being unable to stop taking a drug of some sort?" Tif offered.

"Partly. It's a bit more complicated than that, though." Newt took a deep breath. "Did you know that most addiction problems begin during adolescence?" Both Tif and I shook our heads. "Kids often do things to fit in with groups, to avoid feeling socially anxious or awkward. Inclusion leads to feeling relaxed which leads to having fun. And that's when it starts. The brain is wired to try and make us feel good. So it repeats activities that achieve that. And unbalanced repetition leads to addiction. I bet you played a lot with yourself as a kid."

"And you didn't?" Tif questioned.

"Not as much as you, I bet." She smiled.

"That may go some way to explaining your frigidity." He smirked.

"Just because I can go without doesn't make me frigid. It means I control my desire; my desire doesn't control me." Tif remained silent and she continued. "This guy, in the US I think it was, ran an experiment on addiction with monkeys. He got a mix of subordinate and dominant monkeys. Then taking one monkey at a time, he placed them in a cage next to a group of unfamiliar monkeys. They couldn't touch each other, so there was no physical stress. But the unfamiliar monkeys could group together and scream at the lone monkey. Afterward, each monkey was taken back to another cage where it could relax and pull one of two leavers. One leaver dispensed food. The other cocaine. The subordinate monkeys took much greater quantities of cocaine than the dominant ones. Finding the stress hard to manage. And craving a shortcut to feel better."

"So what does that prove?" Tif asked.

"A few things. It showed that the dominant monkeys had heightened brain activity in the acknowledge pleasure regions, thriving on the challenge from the unfamiliar monkeys. They got a natural high. While the subordinate monkeys showed greater anxiety activity. But more poignantly, it showed that every monkey could survive the situation. It was only when they were alone that each exhibited different behaviour. Much like human addicts. We are not always what we seem. Most addictions are serviced behind closed doors."

"Hey! I'm exactly what I say I am. I hide nothing!" Tif declared.

"We both know that's not quite true, don't we? When there is someone that can be hurt by your actions and they are unaware, then you're hiding." Tif remained silent. "You are addicted to sex. I mean, desperate to lose your virginity, you used an expired condom!" She accused.

"Yes, that was stupid." I joked.

"I don't need you against me too, mate!" Tif stared at me, wide-eyed.

"Then you've got the whole Miss Psycho escapade. I can accept that she seemed slightly deranged, unstable, but did you ever completely analyse your own actions to see how you may have led her on? Her response may have been several shades of insane, but did you do anything to give her cause for expectation?"

"I didn't do anything! That was all her and it was very traumatic!" Tif reminded Newt that he had been a victim to Miss P's lingering emotional torment. Not the other way around.

"I hear that. But there's always at least two sides to a story. Besides, it's not all your fault. Part of addiction is gender-driven. Women are socialised to be connected and expressive. Men not so much."

"Do you really think this is a good time to discuss male repression when we have a friend who is struggling to understand himself, but open to talking and in need of our help?" Tif challenged the implied gender demeaning direction of her comment.

"It makes it more relevant to raise because it's something that may bind the two of you together to some extent." She looked at us both in turn. "Men don't generally talk. Not about themselves anyway. They fail to speak the truth about the dark and jagged emptiness that consumes them."

"There's no dark, jagged emptiness consuming me, dear." Tif retorted.

"You say that, but your behaviour suggests something else." She shrugged. "It's not uncommon for a man to act out to try and feel self-esteem. And what better way than to find yourself atop a woman, furrowing your manhood inside her. I'm sure that must be a power play to elevate even the most depressed soul. At least temporarily, until you reflect on the inequality of your actions and shame presses down on you like a tonne of bricks."

"I don't feel any shame!" Tif stated.

"Maybe you don't. I'm not sure. When you recount your endeavours, you do place a high emphasis on the mutuality of the encounters. Although I am yet to hear you speak of a woman tying you down. A woman taking the lead. It's always you who plays the dominant. They may agree to it, but your addiction is control. The power to convince. To take." Tif remained silent. "Are you depressed as well? I accept you may not present it externally, but covert depression is a well-acknowledged issue with men. Acting out sexually is a recognised marker. Some sex addicts see the act as a magic elixir that transforms them from a state of helplessness to one of omnipotent control."

"Okay. That's me told. Maybe we should get back to Ethan!" Tif's tone was subdued, but Newt ignored the proposed redirection.

"That said, you are an oddity of the addiction model. You're not completely lost!" Newt smiled reassuringly. "Addicts generally have at least five behavioural characteristics. An inability to consistently abstain from misusing a substance, impaired behavioural control and unquenchable cravings for their substance of choice. And they begin to have dysfunctional emotional responses as well as a diminished recognition of significant problems with their own behaviours and interpersonal relationships. You don't really show all of these when you recount your engagements. It's not just any gratification you seek. There is a quality dimension to it that keeps you tied to a skewed form of morality, I guess. That is, a morality in absence of the one huge deception."

"Back to Ethan!" Tif asserted again. Newt ignored him once more.

"It's a trap, really. The sex brings joy. Once the addiction is treated the depression is released. That's usually a double-edged sword. The subject either falters and returns to the elation of addiction or has to find the strength to deal with the depression. This frequently lies in some childhood trauma."

Tif was about to try and redirect her for a third time when he got distracted by some movement on the other side of the bar. It was Addi arriving.

ADDI THE ROMANTIC

David Addison—Addi to his friends—was a middle-aged dad, husband, hopeless romantic and all-round decent person. Unlike many of the group, he wasn't named after anyone, but despite the absence of a deliberate act, he bore surprising resemblance and characteristics to his eponym from the Blue Moon Detective Agency *in the '80s award-winning television show* Moonlighting. *He was witty, entertaining, and with that, slightly immature. That was probably why his kids loved him. When they were younger, they called him 'fun dad'. They would play games together without regard to their surroundings. Sometimes after getting back from pre-school, they would jump up and down on the sofa, dancing to music, laughing and occasionally falling off onto the cushions they had strewn across the floor. Once the sofa springs had been destroyed, they had changed the game to wiggly worms. This entailed collecting up every pillow, cushion and duvet in the house and piling them in a heap in the playroom. Then, diving in, they would wiggle through the layers like worms. As young children, they'd had an inordinate capacity for imaginative fun and Addi had thrived on their energy.*

Addi was the honest lover amongst our group. He loved the world, loved to travel, loved observing and understanding new cultures, and believed wholeheartedly in the goodness of humankind. An idealist through and through. He was considerate, affectionate, tactile, attentive and engaging. In fact, you could pick any positive adjective and it would stick to him. But the danger of approaching the world in such a way, with an innate belief in the high ethics and morals of humanity, was that it was akin to wearing his heart on his sleeve. Which left him continuously exposed. Vulnerable to those around him of lesser character. Despite that vulnerability, the love he shared for and with his family always carried him forward. Granted him sanctuary when he was taken advantage of. Comforted him through emotional turmoil. And protected his soul from the callous and harsh world. The real world.

Unlike the fictional David Addison, Addi had a casual sense of fashion. He had found the love of his life and felt no compulsion to dress well for anyone but her. In general, he would wear jeans with a t-shirt, waistcoat and a pair of rigger boots.

Addi had played the optimistic devil's advocate to Newt's realism over the years, providing emotional counterbalance to our group discussions and to her blunt black-and-white portrayal of society. Neither of them would ever concede to the other's perspective, remaining true to their own polarised belief systems, so silence was the shape of their surrender. In some respects, they made the perfect friendship. One providing explanation and rationalising the suffering, pain and injustice witnessed daily. The other highlighting the joy, generosity and selflessness that all too sporadically unified humankind into a beacon of light in support of the oppressed and afflicted. Newt was the Yin to Addi's Yang.

Addi was my oldest friend. We have shared so many good times. Grew up together since primary school and, as a result, have borne witness to each other's evolution. Whenever I'd been in doubt or in conflict in my youth, Addi had been there to provide solace, to protect me from external forces, wrap me in a metaphorical blanket of love and show me that I never stood alone. He had always been a conscience compass in my life and was beyond reproach in every regard. He was

82

an inspiration to me. To expand on how inspirational in the art of love he was, let me recount just some of the things he had done for his wife. I'll skip over the details of how he proposed, because every person worth their salt steps up their game for that event. It's with the accumulation of the years spent together that thoughts and continued expressions of love matter most.

For example, he took his wife to New York for a long weekend for their first wedding anniversary and, at the top of the Empire State Building shrouded in fog, gave her an eternity ring. Dropping to one knee, he'd reached up and handed her a gold band with a line of alternating diamonds and emeralds. Many people might dismiss the true depth of affection from this act with a flippant 'So what?' To which I would expand on the level of thought embedded within that simple gesture. During their time together they had watched many movies, with a particular soft spot for Saturday morning classics from the '60s. One such movie was 'An Affair to Remember'. The Cary Grant and Deborah Kerr movie that had provided the foundation for 'Sleepless in Seattle' some thirty years later. 'An Affair' recounts the unfortunate situation where an engaged man finds himself falling for an engaged woman as they sail westbound across the Atlantic. Before they disembark in New York, they pledge to meet atop the Empire State building in one year's time, if they still feel the same way about each other. Suffice to say, the movie represented a love as strong as Addi and his wife's, and the sentiment for meeting at the top of the Empire State to affirm their love had been a good enough reason for Addi to make his eternal declaration there.

Another instance of their love was on their tenth wedding anniversary. At this point, their children had been born, so travelling to exotic destinations wasn't a luxury they could afford. However, that

83

didn't mean Addi was going to let the event be mundane. Arranging a picnic with champagne in their home garden, he'd settled his wife on a rug outside while he went back inside and gathered his children together. Then, one by one, he sent them outside carrying a single red rose. Bringing up the rear of the procession, he had presented a small box, which contained a solitaire diamond ring mounted on a platinum band. For their twenty-fifth anniversary, he'd designed twenty-five gifts to give her through the year. One gift for each year of their marriage. Some were simple presents, some were things he had made, and some were experiences. Designed with love, each of the gift's purpose was to make her happy. Yet it wasn't just at the big events that he excelled. It was also in the small details. Yes, he often told us that he bought her flowers every once in a while, and not just when he had done something wrong. He also compiled two CDs for her every year. Yes, very old school! And definitely no lazy playlists! One CD embraced all the new music that was coming in the year and the other was a special collection of songs he would arrange for a Valentine's Day edition.

It was Addi's overt affection that acted as a counterbalance to the sometimes-blinkered opinions of our posse. He was our heart. The one in our collective who ensured compassion, empathy and emotional understanding were not permanently evicted by Newt's structures or Tif's frequently terrifying moral absenteeism. He was our goodness!

COCAINE AND COLLECTIVISM

"Addi!" Tif called out. "Get over here quick!"

Addi smiled and approached us, looking relaxed. "What's up guys?" He shook hands with Tif and I, then went to hug Newt.

"Don't hug her!" Tif protested. "She's been having a go at me all night!"

"I'm sure she hasn't. Our Newt's intentions are always well positioned." Newt smiled at Tif as Addi cheerfully sat down.

"What? Like accusing me of being a sex addict?" Tif declared.

"Let's be honest, mate. That's not really a huge leap in judgement, is it?" Addi smirked. "I mean, you are the one we vicariously live through in that regard."

Addi always had a way of diffusing situations through simple honesty. Stating facts, without casting judgment or offering advice on how to change. He just accepted people as they were and tried to enjoy their company. I knew it didn't mean Addi agreed with the course Tif took with his flagrant disregard for relationship bonds and use of the opposite sex. I also knew Addi understood it wasn't his life to dictate or his actions to live with. While it was certainly entertaining for all of us to listen to the fantastical situations Tif had found himself in, they were always devoid of love. Absent of any real emotional connection. And for that, they held no allure for any of us, but especially not for Addi who believed unwaveringly that love had to be the forbearer of physical interaction. He often said that, without love, everything was just people using people. But that wasn't his thing; his values set deeper in his psyche.

"Thank you, Addi!" Newt resounded triumphantly.

"Yes. Thank you, mate." Tif muttered under his breath, looking betrayed while crossing his arms over his chest.

"I don't know if you are an addict though." Addi acknowledged the tension between them and tried to placate the situation further. "I've always thought you just want to feel like you belong. That you have something to contribute. That you're good at something."

"Hey, I'm good at my job!" Tif defended.

"I wouldn't know, you rarely talk about your work! So I do wonder, is it something you're proud of? Something that makes you happy, to the point of being fulfilled!?"

"Well said." Newt leant her resounding support.

"I'm very happy with my job, thanks. I've had a good career. Just because I choose not to brag about it doesn't mean I'm not proud of it!"

"And yet you can divulge the salacious details of your conquests!" Newt asserted. "Maybe you're not proud of your sexual exploits, so you're trying to justify them? Another trait of addiction."

Silence fell for a moment. I could see Tif felt wounded. He had come out to support me, only to find himself the subject of redress.

"Still." Addi broke the silence. "For clarity again, I'm not saying you're an addict." He gave Tif a reconciliatory smile. "I only wonder why you can't find the peace you clearly want in your normal life. In your work and at home. But what do I know?"

Despite Addi's efforts to lift the conversation up, the awkward silence returned. This time no one dared breaking it. The crux of the discussion was a moral area Tif and Addi would always hold differing views over. Addi had always said that love was, and always would be, a precursor to sex for him. Even if that meant he never experienced some of the more progressive routes to gratification that Tif had, that was fine.

"Forget the addiction. I think there's a lot you and Ethan could learn from each other." Newt declared, eventually ending the silence between them.

"Is it going to be a positive comparison?" Tif worried.

"Depends on how you decide to take it. There is no malice. We came here to help Ethan, not to kick him when he's down." She clarified.

"Let's hear it then!" Tif sat back in his chair, crossing his arms and legs.

"You both suffer self-esteem issues." Newt commenced.

"Give me a break!" Tif was clearly annoyed. "What about my demeanour says I lack confidence?"

"Bravado isn't self-esteem." Newt coldly stated. "Plenty of people use confidence to shield what's underneath. There are in fact two levels of self-esteem. The need to feel respected; which acting confidently can incite. And the need to feel respect for ourselves; for which confidence does little. Ethan is struggling to see people's respect for him, and to respect himself. But he's acknowledged it. Which is why he opens himself up to us. To ask for our help."

"I'm not depressed. So what's similar?" Tif questioned.

"You're not depressed because you're hitting a booty pick-and-mix all the time!" Addi joked.

"Like the cocaine monkey." Newt reminded them.

"What monkey?" Addi was confused.

"Long story."

"Damn right I am getting some fun, but I'm not a junky!" Tif replied.

"No, but you are depressed. Hitting booty is just a plaster on how you feel." Newt suggested. "I think you might be beyond depression, fighting to feel good about life. Instead of focusing on all that offers security and safety, you're seeking joy wherever you can find it." She paused. "Yes, the fun might be amazing. But it's not a foundation for a happy life. There is nothing you can take away from your encounters than perverse memories. These people you share yourself with are neither friends nor family. It's a distraction."

"Right. So you started by saying that Ethan and I could learn a lot from each other. Am I missing something?" Tif's voice was moderately frustrated. "'Cause it sounds like you're just having a go at me again!"

Addi supported him this time. Newt turned towards me.

"Ethan. You should look to Tif. See his confidence. Know that same confidence lays within you. See him engaging with the world and trying to find positivity. Misguided though his direction of search may be." Then turning back to face Tif. "Tif, you should acknowledge the honesty in Ethan calling us up. Sharing with us how he feels. And see that despite his misplaced sense of meaninglessness, not once has he acted in any way that could hurt those he loves. See the strength it takes to do that. Even at his lowest, he still knows what's important."

"And if you are right about me dear, then all of that is great. But are you right?" Tif uttered dismissively.

The uncomfortable silence returned, broken only by the chatter of the adjoining tables and the background music exuding out of the jukebox.

"There are differences between them, you know." Addi took the lead. "Ethan is very much an individualist, he focuses on improving himself. That's why even now, when he is deflated, he sees what he needs to do. Sees himself as the solution provider. Tif's a little different, he externalises his feelings by seeking acceptance from the community."

"You mean a collectivist?" She interrupted, but then she noticed our puzzlement. "A collectivist is someone who places the needs of a group above their own. Although not necessarily Tif's most obvious trait, he nonetheless aspires to gain people's approval as much as servicing his own needs."

"I guess..." Addi agreed. "It doesn't really change your comparison of their state of mind, but it does affect how they may approach dealing with it."

"Fine! Let's draw a line under this. I'm not fucking depressed! I'm happy with my life!" Tif was resolute. Addressing Newt directly. "So let's get back to the friend who actually asked for help. Besides, what the hell do you know about how hard life and love can be?"

Despite my issues, I appreciated why Tif might feel under siege. We all knew he had demons to face, but hearing judgement from Newt, however truthful and honest, was tough. Because no matter how she phrased it, or how well-intentioned, it was impossible to ignore the pedestal she stood upon. The truth was that none of them except me knew exactly where she had started. None of them knew the personal pains she had suffered after leaving Northern Ireland, which now framed her *holier-than-thou* morals.

GROWING THROUGH TRAGEDY

Newt had never needed to worry about love. She had met a guy at university and they had fallen head over heels. Love at first sight. He was two months her junior, but it was clear from the start they had chemistry. The problem with chemistry? Reaction rates and volatility can change with the smallest variations in conditions, and their early relationship had been no exception.

She told me once that their arguments had been spectacular and uninhibited by spectators. Though never violent, at times they were so hostile passers-by could have been forgiven for considering them to be enemies. Once, at the height of an evening's hostility, they had walked the four miles home from the union bar at two o'clock in the morning on opposite sides of the street, only for him to lay himself across the inside of the front door, so she couldn't leave in the morning without waking him. With occasions like this, it was no surprise their university friends never believed they would last. But they proved them all wrong.

He proposed after two years spent together. On bent knee at the end of a pier in the small village of Beaulieu-Sur-Mer, on the southern coast of France, with the sun setting behind the mountains reflecting an orange glow off the still water. He'd taken her hand and asked her to be his forever. Her response had not been traditional. Newt had reached down and pulled him back to his feet. 'Get up you *ejit*!' She'd said. Her now husband had never heard the phrase before, so wasn't quite certain of her answer. She had been smiling and continued to hold his hand, but he'd still needed to double check. To this second enquiry, he received the customary 'Yes' he had hoped for. It had been a spectacular night after that. Taking her back to a boat moored in the harbour, they'd drunk champagne on the deck, gazed at each-other and at the stars, and made love to the gentle undulating tide.

A few years later, following their wedding, Newt had told him she knew he was going to propose because of a bulge in his pocket. But nothing mattered at that point. They'd made a home. Found a rhythm to their companionship. And the love had only continued to deepen.

There are some people who are truly meant to be together. Meant to spend every moment God gifts them in each other's company. Individuals who could happily retreat from the world together and not experience isolation because they are so wrapped up in their mutual affection. That was Newt and her man. Inseparable. Unashamedly devoted. Part of the reason for their success, as Newt had explained, was the sense and mutual expression of equality between them, from the instinctive harmony to share domestic duties, the reciprocal support for each other's careers, to alternating turns to hold the position as primary bread winner. When equality like that is discovered, there is generally little left to destabilise the chemical equilibrium. Not even the arrival of kids caused any stress, which they were unable to rationalise and work through. That didn't mean having kids had been an easy development. They had made the decision when they were both in their late twenties. It wasn't that they felt emotionally motivated at that age. It was simple mathematics. They had identified a collective desire to procreate such that there would still be much to live for after their offspring had fled the coop. And when that time arrived, they would still have sufficient physical and mental agility to savour it.

They'd engaged in the baby-making process much like any couple who had made the same conscious decision. Reducing their drinking, ritualistically planning intercourses around Newt's menstrual cycle to optimise the prospects of a baby and so on. It took a few months before good news arrived. Later on, when they would look back on that time, they would acknowledge they may have crafted the perfect timing, though with imperfect and stress-laden emotional conditions. They'd tried too hard. Making a baby wasn't supposed to be a process open to being designed and engineered. Such destiny couldn't be forced. Nature had a part to play. It sought to gift life out of the unconstrained love and affection of two people absorbed in each other. And with best intentioned cruelty, Newt and her husband were taught Nature's lesson. Twenty-three weeks into the pregnancy, their baby died in utero.

Newt told me their world had collapsed for the first time ever that day. Friends and family had rallied around, but the loss was too personal. No matter how well-intentioned the approaches were, all they wanted was to be alone together. To hold and console each other. To grieve together. To be distraught together. To begin to say goodbye to the daughter they would never know. Yet while that first night after the discovery had been emotional, it was the following day which would prove the most traumatic to reflect on for both of them. At twenty-three weeks, their daughter had been on her way to being fully formed. The only way to extract her was for Newt to give birth. Arriving at the maternity ward amongst anxious women in labour and joyous couples celebrating new arrivals, they were taken to a private room in the corner. A room as distant from the impending screams of new life as the staff could offer. In this quiet sanctuary they prepared for what lay ahead. The staff had assured her they would make the process as painless as possible. Although while the physical pain and Newt's emotions could be sedated, her husband had said afterwards that there was nothing they could offer him. He had to watch. See everything she was being subjected to. Witness the birth of their stillborn daughter. Cradle her lifeless body. Kiss her, knowing she would never feel the love he had for her. Let his tears drip on to her forehead, knowing she would never feel the loss they felt for her. He had had to do this alone, because the medication supplied to Newt had left her body and mind numb. She once phrased her state as 'functional, but cerebrally absent'. In some respects, her husband had confessed to her that was the worst part. Not that he was alone in his suffering for a while, but that he would have to go through this again, with her, as her senses returned. Knowing that her cognitive absence from those moments would make it harder for her to reconcile what had occurred. It would shackle her ability to move forward. She had told me it had been for this reason they had decided to have a funeral. To offer a short moment in which, together, they could say goodbye and find peace.

Funerals or cremation for stillborn babies is law for all babies past twenty-four weeks of pregnancy, as was their registration of birth and death. At twenty-three weeks, though, no formal process was required. Besides, many considered it unorthodox to hold a funeral for a life the law failed to acknowledge. They considered the detractors, like the law, heartless and cold. There are many who suffer at the hand of legal interpretation who could lay testament to that. Fortunately for them, their church was not constrained by the same doctrine. For them, life was born at the creation of a cell. While the life had never been witnessed, the church had the heart to see that the parents' shared experiences with their children began the moment the mother felt change.

Newt told me that she always found it difficult to know where to start whenever she tried to explain that event. After all, where did the experience begin? Was it at the birth or at conception? How much of their time had they associated with making a family? This period of reflection was probably variable for every parent. Perspectives immeasurably altered by creed, nationality and gender. Differing beliefs and faith, placing the sanctity of life on unique pedestals of varying heights. But the variations assigned to gender, the distinct phases of emotions each male and female passes through were for many the most significant. However, what is even more fundamental than the simplistic classifications for determining where life begins are the distinct difference in the parents' mindsets, between those who have given life and those who have lost life, even before it has begun. Newt and her husband fell amongst the latter few, who had thrived on the wave of excitement of a growing life, only to be thrown into mental disarray when that life ceased.

At the time, Newt had suggested they consider therapy, but her husband had convinced her of its futility; because no matter how much each of them attempted to persuade the other they were over it, the words would remain a lie. A lie that would fade with time, but one which they could never completely forget. They could never forget the happiness, the joy of acknowledgement or the way they had begun to think for three. The forward planning as they passed nursery schools or consciously left clothes on the shop rack in favour of accruing savings for a university fund. They had reconditioned themselves in anticipation of an overwhelming change in priorities. The highest of such being the re-prioritisation between work and family. Making a life had become so much more important.

A job required diligence, but it wouldn't wither in neglect. It would continue and could be changed. A foetus, on the other hand, required nurturing, protecting and loving. Many fathers would wonder how something that can't be touched could be cherished. Newt's husband had told me once how he had figured out the answer to that, and it was simple. Love the mother. They are, after all, physically connected with the baby. One eats what the other eats. They breathe and tire in tune. He further explained to me that he believed in the emotional link between mother and baby. Such that if he made Newt smile, it would bring happiness and contentment to his unborn daughter. And if Newt had happy dreams, then so too did their baby. Although he also confessed that none of this had helped them rationalise and come to terms with the question, 'Why me?'.

Today, having come to terms with the miscarriage, Newt and her husband would willingly relay their story to any who showed interest. This willingness wasn't an act of self-indulgence. It wasn't an exercise in sympathy-seeking either. Which was why she had never told our therapy group about it. Only me. It was an attempt to let others know they were not alone in the experience. To offer advice on how they reconciled their feelings. And to show others who would be fortunate enough to have avoided such tragedy that it wasn't as clinically simple as they may perceive. Finally, and more poignantly for Newt and her husband, it allowed them to show others that it was an event which significantly affected all genders, not just women.

They would always begin their story by confessing that, in their lives, they had known parents who had lost grown-up children. Indeed, one of Newt's husband's school friends was one such loss, having decided to take his own life. In this regard, their story was in no way comparable to the anguish that parents in that predicament must feel.

What they had been through must only be the foundation stone of reflection and suffering those who lose an older child must endure. But the human race accepts their mournful reflection with greater ease, while still failing to place sufficient value on a life that hasn't seen beyond the realm of the womb. Newt and her husband held the greatest sympathy for those who had lost more than five months of memories. For those who had lost the same as them. They hoped some comfort could be found in their words. And for those who had never suffered such loss, and didn't understand, they offered an opportunity to learn.

Newt had previously told me they had grown a decade in those few months. It hadn't been a desired lesson, but it was one they knew would make them even better parents. Make them better companions. And it was this same growth that made Newt's council so valued. One day she may confide in the others as much as she had in me about her past. Until then, I feared her underlying compassion and desire to help people may continue to be misinterpreted as a blunt attempt to instruct, rather than the heartfelt supportive wisdom it was intended to be.

DESENSITISATION DEPENDENCY

Addi studied me. "So what's wrong, mate?"

"Everything!" Nothing from the gathering had affected my introspective mood.

"That's got to be some weight on your shoulders then!" Addi smirked. "If you keep thinking nothing is going well, you'll never find a way forward!"

"Exactly what I've been trying to say!" Newt chipped in. "Resolving some issues have to be more important than solving others. And you have your health!"

"Why does everyone always say that?" I uttered with a reserved snigger. "I don't even know if that is true!"

"Depression is a medical condition, I get that, but other than that, you're fit?" Newt queried.

"No, I'm not." After a short pause, I explained. "I've been undergoing tests for about ten years now, for my liver and kidneys." None of them knew what to say. "My liver and kidney function blood results keep coming back as questionable."

"Have they found anything?" Addi asked.

I shrugged. "No."

"That's good then!" Newt offered.

"Is it? I've had tests done every couple of years and it always leads to urgent follow-up tests." I looked around the table. "Each time they identify nothing, but the issue still remains."

"So that's good, like Newt said." Addi affirmed.

"Is it good to be locked in a cycle of being informed there's something wrong but having no treatment prescribed?" I gestured towards my pint. "Except the obvious recommendation of abstinence."

"And how's that working for you?" Tif joked, still looking sore from the accusations of addiction levelled at him.

"Not so good." I confessed. "We all need a release somehow. And for whatever reason, I've always seen alcohol as that."

"It won't help though." Newt stated.

"Thanks dear, I think we all know that." Tif condescended.

"I'm just saying! No addiction resolves the underlying causes of pain." Newt said pointedly, looking at Tif. "It still needs addressing."

"Yes, but it does dull the senses a little." Addi sounded like he was attempting to calm the situation again. "We've all had a bad day and gone home and had a couple of glasses. So let's not pretend its abnormal."

"I agree, although I guess there's a difference between a temporary desensitisation and a permanent anaesthetic. I'd be the first to confess that there have definitely been times I've drunk for more than temporary release." The group said nothing. "I know it doesn't help. I know it doesn't resolve the issues of my life. And I know it is probably degrading my less-than-fabulous physical health. But there's only so many battles I can fight. Only so many things I can deal with.

Sometimes the only detachment I can find from what feels like a living nightmare is through drinking."

"So what do you think is driving your behaviour?" Addi asked.

"Like I said, everything. But probably money the most." I answered.

"You make some money though, don't you?" Addi queried.

"Yes. I make money from consultancy, but it's hard fought. And it doesn't employ me full-time by a long way." I clarified.

"So what's the issue?" Tif jumped in.

"I used to earn a lot more, that's the problem." I took a sip of my beer. "Now I earn less than a quarter of that; all the bills are paid from my personal bank account. I never have anything left. And I feel guilty if I take money from our joint account. So I don't. Instead, I just try not to buy anything for me. And that's hard because that's also a form of tension relief. An act of independence which, as daft as it may sound, brings self-esteem." I took another sip. "When you can't do that, it's quite an adjustment."

"You know Jenny would never begrudge you taking money from your savings once in a while. All she ever wants is to see you happy!" Newt stated.

"I know that. But that doesn't make the act any easier." I took a long, deep breath. "I've always contributed equally to our relationship, and though you tell me it's an archaic stereotype, as a man, I feel I need to contribute at least equally."

"That's your testosterone talking." Newt remarked.

"Maybe. But it's hard to fight gender chemistry." I sipped my beer. "When it comes down to it, even though the bills and costs I pay are for the family, I still feel like I expend more than I earn. And that's why I drink. That's why my blood results never improve. I manage organ degradation by finding the strength for periods of abstinence or moderation. I push to substitute alcohol by something else. In a good week its exercise. In a bad week its chocolate."

"Exercise is definitely the best of those two." Newt stated.

"I think he knows that, dear!" Tif condescended once more.

"At least all of Ethan's addictions are better than degrading the soul in the manner you do!" She fought back. "What you do is the worst kind of indulgent vanity. You want women to want you. To accept anything that you do to them." Newt couldn't contain herself. "No matter what you say, your addiction is worse because of how it affects others. You manage your self-esteem by stripping back someone else's!"

"Great, now moving swiftly on!" Addi intervened before Tif could reply. "Back to Ethan! Where is your health at now?"

"The last set of consultant investigations found nothing wrong with either my liver or kidneys. However, he did find traces of a cancer foretelling protein. So now I am on bi-annual blood tests to monitor that."

"Fuck!" Tif couldn't muster any other comment.

"But it's not cancer?" Addi questioned.

"No, not yet." I replied.

"'Not yet' is not cancer. That's good!" Addi asserted.

"Yes, but I still have periodic checks because of the possibility." I contested.

Tif hummed thoughtfully. "I wouldn't be so certain. One thing I've learnt is that when it comes to medicine, we are all lab rats. Science develops through knowledge. Testing you could just be assessing a theory someone has. And you don't know how many real cases have led to that theory. Or indeed, how many with the same trace protein have ever progressed to cancer."

"I can't believe I'm saying this, " Newt announced, "but Tif has a point."

"Maybe. But when it's not you, it's easier to dismiss, I guess."

"Ethan, you need to learn to see the positives." Addi announced disapprovingly.

From the outside, his passive admonishment may have seemed unsympathetic and out of character, but I knew his reaction came from personal experience.

An Emotional Declaration

Addi had been raised in a loving environment. He told me once of how affectionate, supportive and nurturing his parents had been, although each to differing extents. Despite that, whichever way he chose to analyse his childhood, there could only ever be one judgement and that was how blessed he had been.

However, there is a natural shift in the bonds of parenthood, as the flow of support and care reverses direction, such shift proportional to the passage of time and the inevitable earthbound end of the elder. Addi and I had spoken once of how we both acknowledged the inevitability of death from a young age. While he never allowed his parents to control him as an adult, he had increasingly allowed himself to reengage more with them. It was an unusual process, given he had spent several years striving for independence. He had admitted to me previously that he wished he could say this revived parental appreciation had come from some sort of personal awakening, but it hadn't. It had just been fuelled by the universal truth of mortality.

I'd met his father a few times. He had been a giant of a man in every sense of the word. Standing six foot two, with broad shoulders, he was physically imposing. A striking presence equalled by his personality, which filled the room. He was engaging and humorous. Although, like any child, Addi told me in his youth he had analysed his parents and saw egocentricity in his dad. There were times he'd wished his dad would have toned down the charm and let others lead social gatherings. However, as Addi matured, he came to realise that his dad's approach was less born from self-adulation and more from a desire to make those around him feel welcomed, comfortable. His father sought to absorb the pressure of trying to make encounters enjoyable so that others relaxed and engaged more themselves. That way, fun would become almost inescapable.

Career-wise, I knew his dad had ascended to dizzying heights through steadfast fortitude. Leaving the University of Manchester, where he was studying fine art, he'd returned home to Lincolnshire to be near the woman he loved and wanted to marry. Working first for the family building firm and then for his brothers' construction firm, he'd rapidly discovered a natural entrepreneurial ability, combined with a pragmatism that apparently leant itself to all things engineering related. It was also through these formative years that I understood Addi's dad had begun to capitalise on his charisma, being able to adapt his approach to engage with every level of the social spectrum. Which, when armed with specific knowledge, was quite inspirational. He'd deployed these abilities with increasing effectiveness, growing from a casual labourer to the leader of a billion-pound mining business, which at its peak supported over half of the country's energy demands. A true leader.

But as with all great people of any profession, it was during the highs that staying grounded was of the utmost importance. Hubris could only be kept at bay by remaining open-minded, vigilant and objective. So many people inadvertently open themselves to failure in such times and, unfortunately, Addi's father had been no exception. His pursuit of vertical integration down the supply chain had led his Board of Directors to remove him from office. Yet his dogged determination couldn't be suppressed and he had striven for vindication by acquiring a mine with the potential for an integrated power station. The business eventually failed as a consequence of low production and weak commodity prices.

But, undeterred, he'd resurrected the venture out of the ashes, this time gilding himself with a team that could deliver on his aspirations. This second endeavour nearly succeeded, but affected by a government increasingly bent on austerity at the cost of employment and the environment, failed once more, bringing his business career to a close. Certainly not with rapturous applause for the jobs he had preserved or for the personal wealth he had lost in support of hardworking families. Instead, as is characteristic of humanity's nature to focus on the negative, it had ended with the undistinguished bitterness of a creditor plunging him into bankruptcy, and the publicity from the largely by-standing media of the dream he had failed to achieve. It was not a just end for a man who had served an industry to the detriment of himself for three decades. But if Addi's father had ever been lost in hubris, it was then that, according to Addi, he had rediscovered his true self.

It might be considered that this tale sufficiently represented a challenge, yet it had been about halfway through his second attempt at bringing his clean energy vision to life that Addi's father had been diagnosed with prostate cancer. As with too many men of his generation, a medical aversion founded on a belief that it eroded his maleness meant the diagnosis was too late to be defeated, and treatment to hinder growth was the only option. A process he had apparently pursued with inexorable positivity. According to Addi, his father had refused to be a victim or berate himself for failing to act sooner on his suspicions. His approach had been that there was still life to be lived, not to be drudged through in regret. And the inspiration for this fight was his love for the woman he had left university for. Addi's mum. A woman he had repeatedly thanked for, and shared his success with. A woman whom he cherished. A woman who, as Addis' father had always asserted, had stood resolutely by his side and shared his fortunes, good and bad. A woman who apparently had the strength to survive a life of marriage to a man so galvanised with faith in himself.

It was with this history that, as his father's final days had approached, Addi had needed to tell him how he felt. He told me once that he knew it would be impossible for him to verbally articulate his thoughts adequately while consumed with so much emotion; so he had written a letter instead. A letter he had once shared with me. It read:

Dad

I'm sorry for typing this letter, but there are things I want you to know, and in my mind I keep changing how best to say them, which makes a handwritten letter impractical. I also know if I attempted to say these words out loud to you, emotions would take over and you would never get to hear them.

Simply said, you have been an amazing father. The best! You and mum gave me the most incredible childhood, filled with love, opportunities and experience that far too few get to enjoy; and your continued affection, support and generosity through into my adulthood has been endless. Skiing (water and snow), watching motor racing, attending concerts (though thankfully not opera), travelling the USA, summers in France, Sundays at Clumber Park, meeting Jackie Stewart and Michael Schumacher, traditional Sunday lunches at home, weekly trips to the video store, going to the cinema to see Star Wars *six times in a week, playing chess on Sundays, watching England play at Twickenham...and a first-class education through to university. I* regularly reflect on this privileged life, and aspire to better it with your granddaughters. Though you and mum set the bar pretty high, so it will take some effort.

We have shared many adventures together, both as father, son and as work colleagues. We may not always have seen eye to eye in everything, but I've always respected your opinion, even though sometimes I may have been less than eloquent in expressing that fact. Through all the good, bad and tough times, I have enjoyed every moment and will always remember them with the greatest affection until the day I catch up with you.

There are many words I would use to describe you that you should know: tenacious, inspirational, respectful, caring, loving, generous, supportive, proud and humble. You have carried yourself with dignity and respect at all times, but never more so than the past few years. I have and will always admire you and be proud to call you Dad.

When I started writing this note it was a way for me to share how I feel about you, but I want you to know that you also have a daughter-in-law who has seen and appreciated your love and generosity. And though I know I am saying this on her behalf, she is proud to have called you her father-in-law.

You also have three granddaughters who love you and will miss you more than you realise. You and I may not always appreciate the less-than-sugar-coated truth that youth generally feels at liberty to dispense, or their increasing aversion to displays of affection, but it is something adults have to deal with. It doesn't detract from the love I know they have in their hearts for you. So try and have a little smile knowing they will need to deal with that same crap one day.

Every time we have parted over the last few months, I have hoped and prayed that it would not be the last time I would sit by your side and share your company. Although I cannot feel it directly, I know how much you are suffering and I need you to know that I don't want you to suffer more than you want or can endure. To say I will miss you when I can't be with you is an understatement, but the family you helped forge will get through it together, the same as we have done in the past with you. It may take a little longer than usual, but we will get there. And I know how much you worry for mum, we all do, but you know she has two sons, five grandchildren and two daughters-in-law who will look after and protect her for you.

So at the risk of repetition, you have truly been the most amazing father.

Always your loving, grateful, thankful and blessed son.

The day he had given his dad the letter was the last day he had seen him alive. Addi and his family were supposed to be going on their summer holiday and Addi knew that, if he went, he wouldn't be there at the end. But he told me his father had insisted they go. Addi believed his dad knew it was also the end and didn't want his son to witness the final decline. So, like Newt, Addi had experienced a loss that changed him.

Learn and Step Up

"I wish you could see the gift life is!" Addi stressed. "Once it's passed, none of us knows what comes after!"

"That would be the afterlife and heaven." Newt interrupted, but Addi uncharacteristically brushed her comment off and continued.

"You need to take advantage of every opportunity, not wallow in despair at what might happen! You don't have cancer. Embrace that!"

Tonight it seemed like Addi was resolute in his desire to make me see sense. Perhaps he was thinking of those last moments with his dad and his emotions had been stirred. But I was still entrenched in negativity.

"I nearly died once." Tif proclaimed. "Or at least I thought I might."

"Is this going to be a helpful story?" Newt expressed cynically. "You know, one for the grown-ups?"

"Oh, just get off my case and let me speak!" Tif snapped.

Addi, true to form, intervened to placate the dialogue. "Come on then. What was this near-death experience?"

"I was on this plane, flying to Dusseldorf for a meeting. It was when one of those Atlantic storms was hitting Europe. High winds and rain. So much so that despite boarding the plane, you didn't know if you were going to be allowed to take off." He took a moment to think.

"Everyone seemed on edge. There was this Filipino lady who was really nervous. Short with petite features."

"We don't need yet another female described in infinite detail, thank you." Newt curtailed his narrative.

"Fair enough. Let's just say she was cute." Tif smirked. "Anyway, she was struggling with her bags down the staircase to the departure gate, so I gave her a hand. She was trembling and I felt sympathy for her, so chatted a little. Discovered she lived in Germany and was a *masseuse*."

"Unnecessary commentary. Do we really need to know her occupation?" Newt sounded frustrated.

Tif glared sideways at her and continued. "So we sat on the plane, although still on stand at the gate for about two hours, expecting to disembark at any time. Eventually, the weather cleared. The cross wind weakening enough to allow the tower to shuttle planes off the ground one after the other. But no sooner than we were airborne than the wind returned. We took a lot of buffeting as we climbed above the clouds, some of the worst I've ever experienced. But once we levelled off, things settled down."

He paused. "The majority of the flight was fine, but as we started our descent, the captain announced that the weather had deteriorated and we were in for a bumpy ride. It turned out to be an understatement. We hit air pockets that dropped the plane so hard the seatbelt cut into my lap. When closing in on the runway, we had to fly at an angle because of the wind. Honestly, I could see straight down the runway out of my window seat. It was insane! All the while, there was this little boy on the plane screaming at his mum, 'We're going to die mummy! We're going down, we're going down! We're all going to die!' Nothing like keeping calm!"

Addi grinned sympathetically.

"With the view and the air of panic being stirred by the kid, I sat there thinking he could be right, this could all go horribly wrong. My life didn't flash before my eyes or anything, but I did consider that could be it for me! In the end, the landing was horrendous. Touching one wheel down before pivoting the plane round to line up with the runway and drop the second wheel. When the nose of the plane hit the tarmac, everyone applauded. Very American I know, but I guess myself and the Filipino weren't the only worried ones."

"Is that it?" I asked, uninspired.

"Yes, pretty much. Except to say that, when we got off, I bumped into the masseuse again and she asked if she could give me a ride to my hotel."

"And there it is!" Newt sighed, clearly feeling legitimatised.

"Hold your horses there dear, I didn't take her up on the offer!" Tif sneered. "But it was a close call." He grinned at the rest of us.

Before Newt could say anything, Addi intervened. "I had a similar experience when I was first married. I was flying home to the in-laws. As we were landing, the plane suddenly started to pull back up into the sky just inches from the runway, the propellers in overdrive. Everyone was confused. The captain announced that, as we were landing, the locking light for the landing gear had failed to illuminate. So he wasn't certain the wheels were down or indeed locked into place."

"This already sounds like a closer experience than Tif's." Newt jibed.

Addi continued before Tif could respond. "Anyway, he went on to explain that we were going to do a fly-by past the tower and they were going to look at the landing gear and give their opinion as to whether it looked okay."

"Really scientific approach." Tif joked.

"The stewardesses began talking us through the brace position and got us to practice it as they walked along the aisle, checking each of us in turn." He took a breath. "It took about ten minutes to complete the loop and the flyby, and all the while I was thinking of everything I'd regretted doing in my life."

"That must have been a short thought." Tif mocked.

"And then all I could think of was my family and how if I walked away from that plane, I would do everything I could to make them happy."

"So what happened?" I questioned, slightly more intrigued than with Tif's tale.

"We did the fly-by, the captain announced that everything looked good, but they still wanted us to get into the brace position. As the plane lined up for our third descent to the airport, the words came over the tannoy. *Brace, brace, brace.* My heart raced as I hunched forward, hands overlapped behind my head, elbows tucked into my cheeks. I've never been so terrified!"

"But everything went okay?" Newt questioned.

"Evidently." Tif remarked.

"Yes. We touched down and everything was fine. As we turned back towards the terminal, though, I could see all the emergency vehicles along the side of the runway."

"That must have been awful!" Newt sympathised. Addi nodded.

"But you weren't actually in any real danger! The landing gear was down. At least with my experience, the danger was tangible." Tif protested, clearly incensed by Newt's sympathy for Addi when he had received none himself. "Honestly, I can't believe you sometimes!" He stared at Newt, but we all ignored him.

A silence fell over us. I had so many thoughts in my head. Thoughts of death. Personal experiences that, like Newt's stillborn child, I had chosen to keep hidden from the group. But, unlike her, I hadn't disclosed them to anyone. Until now.

"I've been close to death." I announced calmly. "Not by anyone else's hand though. The certainty of death was only ever mine to determine." My friends looked confused. "Suicide." I declared nonchalantly. My present emotional detachment failing to appropriately convey the extremeness of the blunt confession.

"Are you fucking kidding me?" Tif seemed startled. I shook my head as if to say, 'unfortunately not'.

"It was a few months ago." I took a deep breath knowing that wasn't completely true, as my thoughts of earlier this evening attested to. "I'd love to say I'm completely over it, but that would be a lie. The thought still lingers. Not daily, but it's there."

Nobody knew what to say. Despite all the revelations of the evening, this one left them dumbfounded. To be fair, I had dropped the confession like a new Beyoncé record, without any warning.

"How far did your thoughts progress?" Newt offered compassionately.

I paused. It was one thing to confess to my confidants that I had considered suicide, but to divulge the extent to which I had investigated it would be wrong. The admission itself was an act of sharing that demonstrated I had chosen to move beyond such desperate thoughts. To now explain the depth of the analysis I had undertaken would have only served to introduce questions of how far I had really withdrawn from the idea. Besides, suicide wasn't a group discussion, unless it was mass suicide, but that usually had a lead organiser who took care of the how, where and when.

My group didn't need to hear there were seventeen acknowledged primary methods for taking your life. Most people generally gravitate to just a few, like wrist cutting. Overlooking the fact that it has a very low success rate because the pain from cutting oneself usually leads to hesitation and, if it doesn't, the time it takes to bleed out sufficiently raises the chances of being found first. Worse still, if the attempt fails, the residual affects like tendon damage or ulnar and median nerve damage can diminish sensory or motor ability or even result in lifelong chronic pain. I had considered slitting my wrists. However, two things led me away from it. The first was the very tangible possibility it wouldn't succeed. Secondly, but more importantly, it wasn't a way I would want my family to find me. My loss would be tough enough without leaving a legacy of scared imagery. This same judgement existed for ritual or ceremonial cutting such as the Japanese *Seppuku* or the Aztec and Mayan self-decapitation. These options would also be far too painful and messy.

I had briefly considered poisoning, but the success rate of prescription drug overdoses was disastrously low and catalytic converters on cars nearly precluded carbon monoxide poisoning off exhausts these days.

Then, there was self-strangulation. Although this practice had far too much of a sexual connotation for consideration and I didn't want my ending to be misconstrued. Besides, while mostly effective if done from a sufficient height, hanging would leave traumatic memories for my family. It also held a long history of association to revenge and establishing a foundation for returning to haunt those left behind. I wouldn't want anybody worrying about that.

Beyond the challenges of getting a firearm in the UK, death by gunshot wasn't appealing, just as jumping in front of a train wasn't. Both were far too violent. Besides, I'd been caught on a train five times in the past year because some poor soul had chosen this way out. My lasting memory of those events, other than my prayers for the unfortunate, was the largely unsympathetic chorus of my fellow passengers.

Driving my car off a cliff, while practical, was wasteful in that the car would be written off. That may seem daft, but the car could be sold and afford my family comfort that they may otherwise have to forego.

Self-immolation had some traction in certain geographies, but seemed an excessively painful way to go and was more akin to martyrdom. Similarly to many of the other options, it was also guaranteed to yield a closed casket funeral. Death by volcano unusually fell under this category which, oddly enough, I discovered had become a thing for a while after Kiyoko Matsumoto took her life by jumping into the crater of Mount Mihara in 1933. The coverage of the event had been so high that 944 people jumped into the same crater the following year. As a method, it had merits. No mess. A guaranteed success. Pretty much instantaneous. On the downside, the cost to get near an active volcano from the UK was financially prohibitive.

117

I had been surprised during my research to discover that death by animal attack and by disease were also listed as credible methods. The former involving placing oneself in harm's way with a predator such as a crocodile or a bear. The latter instigated by deliberately seeking to contract an untreatable disease, such as AIDS. When I learnt this, I naturally assumed such choices could only be the preference of those seeking to ensure insurance pay-outs for their families. Insurance claims often being queried as a result of pre-conditions or death by unnatural causes.

There were more discrete methods, such as dehydration or starvation, but these took time and visible signs of degradation would appear long before the desired demise.

All these methods eliminated, I had been left with one that if going for, seemed the optimum approach. The one that had occupied my daydream earlier. Drowning. Leaving a pile of clothes on a beach and swimming out into the sea. Swimming until the temperature stopped my heart or my muscles cramped and I sunk down into the deep. At least that way there was a point at which it became out of my control. I didn't have to inflict the pain on myself. And the chances were that, when the cold took me or my muscles cramped, I would be so tired and numb, that slipping into the deep would feel like a blessing. Yes, that's how far I had progressed my suicidal scenario planning. Though I knew admitting all this to my confidants in addition to the candid confession I'd already imparted might impede their support of me tonight, especially when I had mostly managed to supress such ideas. So I kept it brief.

"Too far." I admitted. "I'd considered things I needed to do to make sure my affairs were 'in order' as they say. And I'd considered how."

"Jesus..." Tif said, incredulous. "That's fucking dark!"

"Desperate." I corrected him.

"What made you change your mind?" Addi asked.

I could offer no response to Addi's question. I didn't know. An unfortunate side effect of my present state of emotional numbness was my lack of clarity to provide an explanation. So I couldn't say any more. An uncomfortable silence resumed. My friends were digesting the information, potentially realising only now how low I had slumped.

"I've never had cause to consider my death..." Newt announced. "But I have felt loss." Everyone remained quiet, including Tif. All somehow sensed that what was to come wasn't joke-worthy.

I could see Newt was composing herself, sourcing the strength to overcome the inevitable emotions that might try to consume her.

"A few years ago, we lost our first child. A daughter. She died inside me."

All looked shocked at the revelation. A wave of sympathy for her rushed in and both Addi and Tif gathered to demonstrate their support.

"I'm so sorry Newt." Addi reached out to hold her hand.

"Me too." Tif added.

"It's a long time ago, now. Nearly twenty years." She sighed. "There's an unimaginable pain that comes from losing someone close, it's impossible to conceive until it happens to you. An emptiness that takes a long time to fill..." She paused. "My life has never truly been at risk, despite growing up where I did. But I have walked with death. I have walked alongside my husband as he carried our baby's coffin into the church. Held his hands as the priest talked of life and loss. We

119

sobbed inconsolably as her small white coffin was lowered into the grave. Words can never convey how that feels, but it is something that has stayed with me. Not as an emotion to dwell on, but as a reason for going forward. For cherishing all I have with my husband."

No one spoke. Two huge revelations in a row was a lot to digest. As for me, to say something would mean I'd have to genuinely feel something different inside me. And I didn't.

"What I'm trying to say is that death, self-inflicted or natural, is hardest for those left behind." She looked at me with sympathetic yet stern eyes. As if to say, *I know how you might feel, but suicide is not an answer.*

It is that moment that the final member of our collective chose to arrive. Swaggering confidently across from the front door, Hawkshaw pulled a stool out from under the table and perched on top of it.

Hawkshaw the Entrepreneur

Hawkshaw Smythe was an interesting character. Of an athletic build, he was an adventurer with an insatiable appetite to savour life. To suck every drop of experience he could get from what he accepted was a brief existence.

Named after an early 1900s comic strip called Hawkshaw the Detective, *he was similar in some respects to the lead character, originally called Sherlocko, who had a voracious curiosity and a vast knowledge of human nature. Similarly to Sherlocko, Hawkshaw considered that life was about the journey, savouring each moment, the exhilaration from each advance or experience; it was not just about the destination. In the end, he believed the destination was the same for all of us. 'Why worry about death and consume the time you have with thoughts of when you will be no more?' A similar declaration to this had been made by one of Hawkshaw's favourite artists. In a song entitled 'The Ballad Of Me & My Friends', Frank Turner sings 'But if you're all about the destination, then take a fucking flight. We're going nowhere slowly, but we're seeing all the sights.' Hawkshaw often told us that nothing was unachievable. He was innovative, challenged the status quo, embraced change and thrived on creativity. He was the vitality of our quintet. The one who espoused possibilities. He believed the only constraints to achievement were the shackles he chose to place on himself, so he didn't.*

As a result, he had seen and done so much. He was fond of telling us how, at twenty-two, he had sat on a balcony in the south of France with the lead singer, guitarist and songwriter from the Moody Blues, Justin Hayward. Moody Blues had formed in 1964 and sold over seventy million records worldwide. Justin was there because Hawkshaw had become friends with his daughter a few years earlier. That night, they had sat and taken turns in singing songs. Justin had, by request, sung 'Nights In White Satin', a song he had sold the rights to for a pittance at the start of his career, and which would later become one of the songs considered synonymous with the band's fame. Hawkshaw, in all humility, had sung back to him 'A Miner's Prayer', from country music artist Dwight Yoakam. Hawkshaw's voice was not devoid of harmonies. He had been a head chorister in the school choir and once sang in an invitation choir at Westminster Abbey. Though for reasons which need not be explained, his range and tone hadn't compared to the professionally-polished vocals and control of his companion.

Four years later, upon his turning twenty-six, he had attended the premier of the rejuvenated 'Star Wars: Episode IV' in London—the 'Special Edition'. He'd strutted in his dinner jacket along the red carpet that night, with a stunning long-haired brunette by his side. They'd walked slowly, absorbing the frenzied song of the crowd around them and laughing, when they hit the press area and overheard a journalist shout, 'Who's that?', followed by another's reply, 'They're nobody!'

The response was irrelevant, though. They were 'nobodies' framed by the context of Hollywood celebrity. But 'nobodies' on the red-carpet side of the velvet rope and evidently looking sufficiently the part to have their status questioned. Inside the theatre, they had directly sat three rows behind George Lucas and Mark Hamill, and one row in front of Brian May, the lead guitarist from the rock band Queen. For a nobody, he was doing just fine.

At thirty-four, he had found himself walking through the front door of No. 10 Downing Street to attend a meeting with the Prime Minister's advisors regarding the need for state support to deliver clean energy infrastructures. He was once again the nobody in the room, but he was nonetheless a parvenu sitting with executives from every major power company in the heart of the nation's government. And he was leading the most advanced and largest clean energy project in Europe.

While he could not argue that some of his experiences had been the product of good fortune and his parents' societal position, there were a great many others he reflected on that were the sole product of his dogged determination to challenge himself and philanthropically aspire for better. This indefatigable determination had developed at a young age. During his second year of university, he became vice captain of a rugby team known for playing the second oldest varsity match in the country. Such a less-than-auspicious position to hold, the second in command of academia's potentially third oldest rugby team. Yet he had held the office with pride. And that year, when his team played that almost-original varsity match, his pleasure had been evident for all to see through the freshly-cut, slicked-back Mohican partitioning his scalp, to the hits he took and the try-saving tackles he made, after sprinting across the pitch to pummel the opponent's winger in to touch two metres from the try line. His team won that day.

Regardless of the limited historical value or notoriety of that event, he often recounted that it was one of his proudest memories of his youth. He had often pondered why that might be and had concluded that it was because he saw it as his first real triumph. Up until that time, much of his success had been on reattempts. But winning that game had been the obsession from the moment he'd marched onto the pitch, and he had been instrumental in its delivery. Leading with his head and heart, he had played to inspire. And afterwards, got thoroughly drunk. Then when the snow had arrived later that evening, in diminished capacity, he had scooped it up in dustbins and buried a Porsche 911 that was parked on the street. Childish, yes, but harmless fun at least. Though he later felt for the owner, who had been tasked with cleaning it off once crusted by the early morning chill.

Hawkshaw always dressed well. Clean-ironed shirts, blazers, waistcoats, polished shoes and hair sculpted with a little clay product. He frequently wore glasses, despite having a contact lens subscription, because they made him feel more assertive. He was always convivial in his demeanour, humorous and relaxed. He had never smoked, and didn't drink anymore, holding a firm belief that they were the worst in household drugs that only clouded reasoning, introduced doubt and bred uncertainty, eventually eroding confidence. That said, there was in fact a slightly longer story to his modern view on alcohol.

Back at university, there had been an annual event called the 'Dirty Disco', which was really just an excuse to get semi-naked and party in mass. A bit like a progressive toga party. Hawkshaw, in all youthful buoyancy, had attended with his girlfriend wearing a pair of mining boots and a jockstrap. He'd drunk so much and partied so hard that night that by the time the DJ pulled the plug on the deck, the underground had stopped running and only infrequent night buses operated. His girlfriend had compassionately invited him to stay with her. She lived only a short walk from their campus, which made the offer seem like a fantastic solution through blurred, alcohol-infused eyes. And with the cold night air infiltrating his trench coat, chilling him to the core, he'd accepted. As with many events life throws, good decisions become most apparent in hindsight. And the following morning, when he awoke with no more clothes at hand and the prospects of a return to his flat during the morning city rush, the optimum decision made six hours earlier became crystal clear. While youthful adventure is rarely challenged by embarrassment, standing on the tube station's platform at seven thirty in the morning, with his head throbbing, he felt very self-conscious. With a trench coat wrapped tightly around him, the belt constricting the movements of the fabric to ensure his waist and torso remained concealed, his naked lower legs protruding from below the hem adorned with mining boots, he exuded all the signs of a flasher, waiting to gift unsuspecting female professionals a morning sight they may struggle to forget. He told us this was the moment when he revaluated the true experimental value of alcohol.

Like Addi, Hawkshaw was an idealist. He didn't see the rigid boundaries of the world, just obstacles that had yet to be overcome. Focused, driven and full of energy, he directed all at whatever entrepreneurial endeavour he was working on, repeatedly delivering action after action in pursuit of what many said were unrealistic goals.

Like Newton, he never switched off. If he thought of an idea, he would write it down or send himself an email. Then, at the earliest opportunity, he would begin crafting and shaping the idea into something worth delivering. He wasn't a fool and would always interrogate a scheme before etching it into his list of things to do. But if his drive had one flaw, it was that he believed passionate action was enough to succeed. He refused to acknowledge the politics of society which must be navigated. He believed the integrity of actions would always speak louder than their detractors. This was a sentiment he relentlessly urged others to adopt, as if he'd made it his goal to challenge and push everyone. Determined that all he knew would 'suck the marrow out of life' as Henry David Thoreau had once written. Or as was read at the commencement of every Dead Poets Society's meeting.

With that analogy in mind, just like the movie's lead characters John Keating and Neil Perry, he epitomised free will and aspiration.

Born Resilient

Hawkshaw was very much like Newt's husband. He was confident, adventurous, though a little *gung-ho* at times. However, like Newt's husband, somehow his confidence always seemed to ensure the *gung-ho* worked out. It was because of this similarity that Newt spoke a little less when Hawkshaw was present and rarely found cause to disagree with him.

"So where are we at?" Hawkshaw challenged exuberantly. "Sorted him out yet?" He gestured towards me.

"It's a work in progress, I think." Addi replied.

"I thought you'd be further than 'a work in progress'! What you all playin' at?" He jibed.

"It's probably more complex than we thought..." Newt offered.

"So complex we're struggling to agree on any recommendation!" Tif quipped.

"Well, never fear, I'm here!" Hawkshaw oozed determination. "Someone fill me in."

Addi took the lead. I guessed he was seeking to avoid reigniting a conflict between Tif and Newt. He talked through my issues, the jobs, the money, the drinking and the depression. For whatever reason, he skipped over my suicidal declaration. And, to keep things concise, he only briefly mentioned Tif's advocacy for sexual relief and Newt's more structured philosophy to happiness.

"So, basically, and stop me if I'm off base, you're fucked in the head!? You're assessing your competence based on other people's opinions, you're assigning a monetary value to self-esteem, you're accepting a lack of control to chart your future, and you are infusing that acceptance with the demon drink." Hawkshaw took a breath. "Is that about right?"

They all nodded.

"Well, I'd start by telling you other people's opinions are generally worth shit!" He stared intently at me. "I mean, we all know about my chequered career! I've been judged nearly every day of my working life and do you see it affecting me?" He momentarily waited for acknowledgement and when none came, carried on. "Of course you don't! And you know why?"

"Because you don't give a fuck?" Tif offered.

"No. Though that is true!" He smiled. "It's because I see people for what they are. I see through the words and the body language and judge their worth. You might say that makes me as bad as them, but the difference is, I don't feel compelled to say anything. I don't try to change them. That doesn't mean I don't accept them either. Life is too bloody short for trying to save everyone's soul!"

"A bit harsh to just give up on people." Addi suggested.

"I haven't given up on everyone, but there are people, especially in the professional world, who are beyond saving! They've been entranced by the lure of money and there is no easy salvation from greed."

"So you simply dismiss everyone at work?" Addi pushed.

"No. Like I said, I've just learnt to read behaviours." He shrugged. We all looked a little bemused. "Look, there are good people who work. In fact, the majority of people are good, I call them the 'squeaky clean'. But as with everything, even in a fruit bowl, there are a few rotting apples. I put these 'spoilers' into three categories: the bullies, information withholders and the ass-kissers. They're all bad in different ways. They all work to disadvantage others."

"I can tell you're going to love this, Newt!" Tif joked flippantly.

"Bullies are the most obvious profile. But I don't think they're the worst. At least, with a bully, you always know where they are coming from. Behaviour is repetitive. And that's what makes it easier to deal with them. Even if you're not that resilient, with time you become used to it. It becomes the norm." He took a moment. "It's not good to see it as the norm, but at least it's a way of living with it. Never been the way for me though. I've too much fight to sit back and accept. But I won't bother seeking to change them, especially if they're my boss. I'll just move me."

"Isn't that just avoidance by another name?" Tif questioned.

"Yes I guess. But it's better than accepting it and suffering!" Tif remained silent. "Then you've got the ass-kissers. These guys will suckle anything, like piglets on a sow's teats. They are the consummate 'yes' person. Anything their boss says is gold. They make others seem disruptive and, because of that, are harder to deal with."

"So what do you do?" Addi prompted.

"Just keep presenting the facts. Facts are usually irrefutable. And, in my experience, always end up casting aside speculation and subjectivity."

"I'd agree with that." Newt supported.

"However, it doesn't work with everyone. The next group are the information withholders. They're the bane of a fact-based debate. They deliberately seek to undermine by sanitising what piece of information is accessible. Some do it for preservation. They make themselves indispensable. Others just do it to undermine their bosses and peers."

"Met a few of those in my time." Tif said. "Without a single exception they were all protecting themselves!"

"What it all comes down to is that life isn't easy. If it were, we wouldn't have a world bathed in inequality. But life can be lived and loved if you abide by two simple rules: never lose sight of what you want and will accept; and never stop believing in your own ability to rise to any occasion."

As was rapidly becoming a trend this evening, silence engulfed the table as Hawkshaw's ideas were being processed.

"I'll give you a couple of illustrations. One of these is my favourite story to tell." Hawkshaw announced.

"Finally! Let's lighten the mood!" Tif sighed.

"I was working in Australia one summer while at university. Got stuck out in the middle of nowhere on this mine, where the pinnacle of entertainment at the weekend was the burger bar and the pub. Although I did meet this great woman called Kylie of all things. But that's a different story."

"I get the feeling it's one I might prefer to hear!" Tif commented, but Hawkshaw let it pass over him.

"I'd been there for two months before hitting the road for a few weeks with some of the other students I'd worked with. It took a twelve-hour bus ride through the night before we arrived in a place called Broome, on the north coast of Western Australia. It was one of the coastal towns where the population swelled threefold in peak holiday season. Though not a patch on Scarborough!" He grinned.

"We'd spent our first day on the beach, had a few beers and went out to the pub that night for a few more. We were having a good laugh when this rotund aboriginal lady comes up to me. And when I say rotund, I mean huge! It would have taken two of us with outstretched arms to circle her! Anyway, she comes up and offers to have sex with me if I want. It wasn't a bashful offer either. In my face, feeling my ass, whispering in my ear. I was twenty and wasn't worldly-wise at all! I took a step away and politely declined her proposal, then turned back toward my friends. Next thing I knew, her husband grabbed my arm and starts shouting, 'What, you don't fancy my wife? She not good enough for you?'" He chuckled at the memory. "There were ten of us, but we all freaked out as we saw these other guys start to form a group behind the husband. It was absolutely terrifying!"

"What happened?" I asked.

"I declared there was nothing wrong with his wife, but that I was happily engaged. And then we all bolted. We didn't stick around to find out if there was more to come."

"So I'm assuming that's an illustration of what you will accept?" Tif asked.

"Of course!" Hawkshaw confirmed.

"It's not a great one." Tif replied. "Not like you really had any dilemma!"

"So what's your other anecdote?" Addi spurred Hawkshaw on, ignoring Tif. "The illustration of rising to an occasion."

"That was back at school. Sixth-formers used to do this thing called the 'gauntlet'. It basically entailed taking the kids from the junior dorm one by one, standing them at the far end of the senior dorm and making them run through it while being bashed with pillows. It was brutal!"

"That doesn't sound so bad!" Tif remarked dismissively.

"The pillows weren't just fluffy, you know. The seniors would push the feathers down into one end so it was densely packed. Then some would swing for your head. Others your chest. And the real bastards your legs. You could try running and jumping to miss the low swings, but it was potluck. The dorm lights were out and only the candescent moon would offer any guide as to where the hits were coming from. You just had to try and stay on your feet and get out."

"That's disgraceful!" Newt protested.

"Back in the '80s, it was just part of being British and growing up! A rite of passage." Hawkshaw declared. "People joke today about boarding schools being bastions of privilege. Back then, they were both bastions of privilege and torture prisons! The gauntlet was just one tool for servitude and discipline. There were others too." He paused, beaming as he reminisced. "We used to have this 'fagging' thing, which was effectively establishment-endorsed-slavery for the sixth-formers. Behaviour was marshalled by the sixth-formers as well. If you didn't do as you were told, they had the power to make you run during your lesson breaks. Having you jog backwards and forwards in front of the girls' house."

"That's atrocious!" Newt said with an expression of disbelief.

"Couldn't agree more!" He said. "We were all growing up in a world in transition, though. What is unacceptable today was normal then."

"Can't imagine you doing what you were told!" Tif stated.

"You'd be surprised! I'm a product of that upbringing. It made me the person I am today. Not saying I didn't fight back, though! I remember I got sent to make a cup of coffee once. I just ran the hot water tap until it was at peak temperature, and made the drink that way. My cockiness lasted about two minutes, though. The sixth-former noticed straight away and gave me an almighty smack. The type of thing you'd get immediately expelled for these days." He looked around reflectively. "Yup, it was a very different world!"

"But you found a way through it!" Addi asserted cheerfully. "Dug deep and rose to the challenge."

"Yes. Had to. When it comes down to it, be prepared to be a fighter and know what you want." Hawkshaw asserted.

"What makes a bully?" I questioned. "I mean, they can't just be born that way?"

There was a moment's pause before Newt replied. "Most people say bullies are raised; they're not made. It's an attribute learnt in response to stress."

"I don't think anybody deliberately sets out to raise a bully, Newt." Tif remarked.

"Don't count on it." Hawkshaw defended her.

Newt didn't require a champion, though. "I'm not suggesting they're taught like dogs, but they learn and are pushed into it passively as a consequence of their circumstance." She took a breath. "There's a variety of things which have been suggested could ignite a bully's temperament. The most frequently cited is a lack of loving or caring parents. Parents who teach their kids that winning at any cost is the only way."

"I knew a few of those at school, that's for sure!" I commented.

"That's not really surprising, is it? Like Hawkshaw, we were at boarding school." Tif observed. "Many a dejected child seems to end up in boarding schools. It's not a decision always made in their best educational interests."

"That's true." Newt resumed. "But it does create an environment that may have a bias towards pushing people in that direction. Just listen to Hawkshaw's experiences. I mean, I can imagine boarding school might feed an exposure to inconsistent discipline, unsupportive peer networks, or abuse. Both could lead to poor academic performances or low self-esteem. All of which are known factors that can develop a bully archetype."

"Yeah, but not everybody responds to those influences in the same way. Else we'd all be bullies, Ethan and myself at the front of the pack." Tif remarked. "And Hawkshaw here too."

"No, not everybody responds the same way. Some people are born with more resilience and find their own way forward without feeling compelled to demean others in the process. Like you three!"

"And the best way to do that is to keep reminding yourself that the bully is the insecure one. Because they can't feel good about themselves without putting others down." Hawkshaw asserted.

FIGHTING THE BULLY

While Hawkshaw talked well about psychology, he was less adept at accurately reading people's characters than Newt. His success and resilience were more the results of continuous scenario planning and interpreting actions and effects. Newt, on the other hand, was not judgmental, but a person couldn't evade her assessment of their worthiness. It was a skill she had deployed to maximum effect in her career and something our group feared she was frequently exercising on us. She had once told me about someone who had come under her watchful eye for assessment, someone who had been a university friend of her husband's. The guy, Glen, came from Surrey. A product of a good education, he had been a classmate of her husband's when Newt met him. Being six foot two, as a rugby player he had a classic second row figure with what initially looked like a scrimmage disfigured face. With dark, poufy, spikey hair and a gaunt, elongated, pale face pitted with the adolescent scars of acne, he bore some resemblance with a Tibetan Mastiff. Newt had never been able to say why, but she had distrusted Glen from the first moment she met him. Friends that exude body language in favour of their mate's girlfriend weren't really friends. His haptics were far too familiar. So while her husband had never noticed anything back then—probably because he had such complete trust in the might of their love—she had observed his desire and it had made her skin crawl. She never deliberately avoided him, but had always made it clear that nothing would ever come of an attempt to gain her affection. She was unavailable.

Blind to the issue, her husband never had cause to question Glen's integrity or friendship. But all rats eventually reveal their nature. It was just a matter of time. Time eventually ran out on Glen, twenty-eight years after they first met. Glen had been working in Brazil for about a decade. Similarly to the glass ceiling of work promotion for Catholics in Northern Ireland during the troubles, expats in Brazil suffered from career discrimination. That said, Glen had advanced to become Director of Strategy for a national minerals company. Within his remit, he had been handed governance over a couple of non-core subsidiaries progressing innovative technologies for low-emission production of metals. To be fair, one of the technologies had prospects. It was low cost, compact and carbon-neutral, emitting net zero carbon dioxide. When the world finally stepped up to place a value on carbon dioxide that equalled its impact on the global ecology, the technology would be in a robust position to benefit.

Newt's husband was working with companies to aid them develop clean technology solutions for energy and industry. One day, Glen had called him and asked if he could help. At the beginning, it was just casual advice. Then the advice grew into reviewing documents and eventually into a request to help identify investment pathways. It was at this juncture that Newt's husband decided the invisible line between friendship and business had been crossed. Rather than providing the information requested, he'd submitted a commercial proposal to provide services. People may have different views on the charity of friendship, but Newt's husband worked for himself and was using his network to progress his existing clients' activities. For him, to offer an equivalent service absent of income would have been ludicrous. Besides, Glen and his company always had the option to decline the proposal and do it alone. But they hadn't. They'd accepted his terms. So he had undertaken the work with exactly the same diligence and professionalism he would have provided for any client. In fact, it was arguable that he went further, gifting unpaid time to ensure everything he delivered was to an optimum standard. But despite this, the relationship had soured by the time Christmas arrived.

Newt recalled an instance when her husband had answered a phone call from Glen one crisp November morning. It wasn't unusual for Glen to call for a catch-up, but his motivation this time was far more purposeful. It was aggravated confession time. He felt aggrieved about having to pay for help from a friend and had done so for some time. Glen had spoken relentlessly, harshly and with an apparent all-consuming disdain. He had clearly spent time considering his narrative, because it flowed continuously from one point to the next, without pause for response. Newt remembered her husband declaring it 'was the narrative of a bully'. But he wasn't one to be bullied.

As the diatribe persisted, he had decided to start taking notes. No sooner had he raised the pen than Glen changed topic, sounding even more agitated. 'Are you writing?' He'd asked. Newt's husband had lied, but that hadn't pacified Glen, who justified his accusation by claiming he was certain he could hear him writing. What did he think, that he had super powers? Glen was calling from a mobile phone some six thousand miles away while walking his dog around the streets of Rio de Janeiro, yet he 'was certain' he could hear a pen moving. Although while the whole outburst had been a surprise, this particular behaviour shouldn't have been. Paranoia was a trait of many bullies.

When the tirade had eventually come to an end, Glen had concluded his speech with: 'You don't need to say anything.' Newt's husband refused to accept that. He had listened to accusations and abuse for twenty minutes, there was no chance such dialogue would be taken without retort. So he gave reply in turn to each assertion made. And, in his conclusion, levelled a statement that demonstrated his personality the best and honoured his integrity and values. 'With our evident difference of opinions, if I have a choice to make between doing this work for you or keeping your friendship, I choose friendship.' He knew the declaration had incensed him further by not yielding in acceptance of his views. Bullies detest being challenged.

He had continued working for the company, completing each task to his high standards and exploring investor interests in absence of supplementary remuneration. All of which had been approved in writing from his client. He could have been forgiven for considering the pre-Christmas abuse consigned to the waste bin, but he would have been proven wrong. One March morning, while waiting in an airport lounge to catch a flight, he received an email from Glen claiming he had breached the terms of his contract with regard to confidentiality. He hadn't. Rather than giving in to panic, he simply wrote back requesting provision of the evidence for his consideration. To reiterate, bullies dislike being questioned, and given their lack of self-awareness and control, they tend to become agitated and aggressive. Within half an hour, a fresh email had arrived in his inbox, setting out the accusations, which at best could have been considered weak suppositions. Unsurprising, given that he was innocent of the act. His response was short: 'Thank you. I will review and revert to you shortly.'

Throughout the subsequent flight, he had pondered what the trigger for such unfounded accusations had been and then it clicked. A legal friend of his had inadvertently met Glen at an investment conference a week earlier. During their conversation, the legal friend had suddenly acknowledged the connection and had inferred that was 'Newt's husband's project'. An innocuous statement for the majority. But for a bully, a pride-stabbing dagger.

138

I do not propose to detail them in full, but the intervening litigious exchanges were numerous. Unsupported assertions from Glen and fact-based, document-supported responses from Newt's husband. With each exchange, Glen's demands escalated, until eventually a conference call was proposed. Glen had invited his legal counsel onto the call, so Newt's husband had decided to invite a witness and obtained consent to record the discussion. The conversation had initially been framed to be around moving forward, but when the opening statements referred to Newt's husband being in the wrong, he refused to let it pass uncontested. He had requested four times for evidence to be provided and, with each request, was rebuffed by the counsel's corporate superiority. It was an approach far removed from one of reconciliation or amicable resolve. Instead, Glen and his corporate gang endeavoured to intimidate him into signing a termination agreement embedded with a gagging order and punitive damages. Newt's husband had elected not to play the game and simply submitted a termination letter under his existing contract.

To say sparks flew would be an understatement. Bullies may not like being challenged, but they detest being outmanoeuvred even more. Then, rather cheekily to rub salt into an open wound, Newt's husband submitted an offer to the chief executive of the parent company to buy the subsidiary. This deeply incensed Glen. Within a matter of days, he received a letter from an independent lawyer threatening to take legal action and instructing him to cease all contact with the business or its owners. The letter was weak, unsubstantiated and unclear as to whom the legal practice was acting on behalf of. When all these elements were requested, the lawyers fell ominously silent.

Three months passed and Newt's husband had received no response to his offer of acquisition, so he followed it up with another letter addressed to the parent company. Again, no reply arrived. Instead, a further lawyer's letter landed on his doormat with more threats, spurious accusations and demands. To which he launched an offensive, asserting that he would pursue the law firm for defamation of character and harassment if they continued to make accusations. They fell silent once more. In absence of a response to his offer to buy the technology company, he'd finally walked away. Many would consider this outcome a success. To some extent they would be right. Newt's husband was a robust individual. But when threatened by one of the largest mineral companies in the world, it would take its toll on anybody, both mentally and physically. Of course, he was no exception. I had heard him once state that he wouldn't have been able to get through an experience like that without Newt. During the whole encounter, she had been there to listen, support, and rebuild him each day. Repair his armour and make him battle-ready. Make him alert. Astute to the delicacy of the proceedings.

Now, like a white knight, she attempted to do this for me. To help me find a position of positivity. Help me find myself. Rediscover a purposefulness that would allow me to grow once more. Make me strong and 'squeaky clean' like her husband. While Tif persisted to encourage me towards distraction. Into more despicable endeavours.

LOOKING FORWARD

"Have any of you ever considered that some bullies are just forcefully trying to bend the rules? Find the grey areas?" Asked Tif.

"It doesn't matter what their purpose is," Newt intervened, "their behaviour is still unacceptable and shouldn't be tolerated!"

"So you can honestly say you've never bent the rules!? Never been less than perfect in chasing a goal?" Tif challenged the group, looking at each of us in turn.

"Yup." Addi declared.

"You don't count mate! Your love drives your integrity! What about you two?" He prompted Hawkshaw and Newt. "No offence, Ethan, but I'm taking you as a given for righteousness, like Addi. It's why you're so depressed! The straight and narrow will do that to a person."

Newt shrugged, shaking her head no in response.

"No. I've never done anything I regretted because it was dishonest!" Hawkshaw asserted.

"That sounds like a dodge to me." Tif replied.

"No. It just means I've done daft things, things where I wasn't thinking." He clarified.

"Such as?"

"At university, I once put my friend's laundry in the dustbin on the day they came to empty the bins."

Tif smirked. "Why?"

"By accident. He'd left it in a black bin bag on top of the chest freezer we had next to the flat's front door. Without checking I'd just assumed it was rubbish and put it out." Hawkshaw explained.

"I bet your friend went through the roof?" Tif looked incredulously at Hawkshaw.

"No, he was surprisingly alright about it! Accepted it was a genuine mistake." Hawkshaw went on. "Didn't change the fact I felt like shit for about a month afterwards. I kept thinking how I'd have responded if the roles had been reversed."

"That was a good friend!" Addi smiled.

"Yes. And he still is today!" Hawkshaw smiled back. "But back to your question, I wouldn't ever deliberately act in a way that would make me think less of myself. Life is too short to be continually looking over my shoulder. I'd just as soon keep looking forward!"

That was true. Hawkshaw was very much about today and tomorrow. He had little time for reflection except to remember experiences he had enjoyed. He would say things like: 'Why look back at the negative events in life. If you've learnt from them, they serve little purpose and distract you from focusing on the times to come.' For as long as we had known him, he had always rolled with the punches and sprung forward with vigour. 'Change what you can change. The rest is just wasted energy.' That was another one of his mentoring phrases.

"Getting back to Ethan's issue, you just need to start accepting that crap happens!" Hawkshaw looked into my eyes. "When the crap is behind you, leave it there. Move on."

"It's true!" Tif concurred.

"I know you've had trouble getting a job," Hawkshaw sympathised, "but you can't let it get you down! I recently lost a contract I was bidding on. Do you know why?" No one answered. "Because I took a meeting sitting in my car and the managing director thought that it was unprofessional!" He pulled a bemused expression. "I might be able to accept that, if it wasn't for the fact the same guy started the video conference while he was driving, then signed off when other participants arrived and re-joined ten minutes later. I mean you can say arrogant, hypocritical, and appalling ambassador for safety! But there's nothing I can do about that!"

"At least you have something tangible!" I declared. "I've been kicked out of a competition at final interview stage because I disagreed with the psychological profiler."

"You don't need to listen to idiots like that!" He dismissed me. "Answer a few questions and they think they can tell you who you are. That's algo-rhythmic bollocks! The brain is the most complex organism in the known universe! These idiots market themselves as providing a service that can profile it in less than three hours. Come on, that can only be considered disingenuous! Every person is constructed from unique DNA. The sample population that is required to provide a reasonable hypothesis of collective behavioural traits associated to the infinite DNA strands that exist would be significant. Let alone amass the sample population required to construct a model that could accurately and reliably profile, and indeed predict such characteristics."

"He's right, you know!" Newt asserted vigorously. "No one can accurately create a profile based on one analysis. Hawkshaw said it, it's just clever mathematics being used to brand what is, at best, a rough and generic profiling method!"

"Yes. They use this thing called fuzzy logic." Hawkshaw highlighted.

"That's right!" Newt took over, looking surprised by Hawkshaw's knowledge. "Fuzzy logic is this approach to computing developed by a guy in California, based on degrees of truth rather than the usual true or false. The issue with such an approach is that, despite such logic being less rigid, the degrees of truth used in the model inevitably represent a subjective bias on behalf of the modeller, which is forever embedded in the functional fabric of the programme. This bias is then overlaid by the interpretive bias of the psychologist. Cognitive bias overlaying cognitive bias to deliver a definitive prediction. An oxymoron to say the least!" She smiled to herself. No one else saw the joke.

"As I said, algorithmic bollocks!" Hawkshaw interjected.

"He is right." Newt continued. "And it is a misfortune of societal evolution that an increasing reliance and responsibility has been vested in such tools for determination rather than deploy and rely upon the conviction of self-judgement by those who must live with the outcomes. It's a shame that these intermediary deities never stand to be proven wrong. It's also a shame that those who are discarded never receive the opportunity to demonstrate their competences and those in receipt of the approved candidates are never exposed to the complete portfolio of talent."

"Fuck Newt, you're like a bloody thesaurus come science journal tonight!" Tif quipped.

"Long and short of it is that it's arguably arrogant and definitely ignorant to say a person can be profiled that quick for the purpose of making a decision!" Hawkshaw attempted to offer his support.

"Maybe. But that's what I have to contend with." I replied. "And it's me who has to reconcile how that makes me feel. Which is hard to do when even your family and friends don't recognise the person described."

"I'll say it again, it's all bollocks!" Hawkshaw firmly restated.

"Bollocks it may be, but that bollocks is a gate I can never get through." I highlighted.

PROSHOLES

I could see that Hawkshaw was the one amongst us who related the most to my work situation. I knew he'd suffered similar predicaments, but had never dwelled on them. He was a firm believer in rolling with the punches and when one door shut, another opened. He merely needed to find the door, yank it open and seize the opportunity. That said, experience had shown him that opportunities were sometimes preceded by a void. A gap filled with job applications and multi-stage recruitment processes. But he never viewed these periods as something to suffer in silence. In fact, he considered them opportunities for new adventures. To complete a task or challenge that few got the chance to experience. He was a passionate, optimistic idealist, if there could be such a person.

"Let me give you another illustration of the optimistic fortitude I aspire to." Hawkshaw started. "I had just turned forty, a delicate age for most people, where acceptance of mid-life status becomes a prerequisite for a happy existence."

"That's probably around thirty for a woman!" Tif joked.

"It is apparently an age where opinion polls suggest most people begin to fear loss of employment. They develop an irrational fear that age begins to become an obstacle to recruitment. Despite there still being twenty-seven years left until retirement." Newt offered. "Which on a standard position churn of three years gives the person at least nine more roles before they could be laid out to pasture."

"Thanks Miss Analytical!" Tif wisecracked.

"I was managing a large infrastructure project. We were hoping to build a low-emission power station, capturing and storing more than ninety percent of its carbon dioxide emissions." Hawkshaw took an uncharacteristically long and deep reflective breath. "The coal was coming from a sister company next door. They had enough stocks to supply us for over fifty years. The only problem was that the mine was consuming more money than it generated revenue and had to borrow resources from the power project to survive."

"I remember you talking about this before!" I announced.

"Then you'll recall me saying how the lending vultures had descended, talons splayed ready to rip apart the business assets in an effort to protect their reputations and recover their cash?"

"Very eloquent!" Tif jested.

"The problem with birds of prey, though, is that they are opportunistic, indiscriminate and seek to act rapidly to feed their needs! Fixed on loss mitigation and debt recovery, they focused on the mine because it had the potential to generate cash." Hawkshaw explained.

"I thought it was losing money?" Addi queried.

"It was, but you can't teach bankers!" Hawkshaw smirked. "Anyway, while they messed around with the mine, we were nominated for over a billion pounds in European funding and had secured an offer to buy the power business that would repay the bank debt and all the creditors."

"You saved the day then?" Tif commented.

"Should have. The banks decided that the offer just meant they could probably get a better offer by putting the parent company into administration and doing a trade sale of the power business."

"Idiots." Tif muttered.

"Like I said, you can't teach bankers. So they ran this sales process and for about thirty minutes the management team bid was nominated as the preferred buyer with an offer that valued the business at a quarter of what the previous offer suggested."

"Cheeky little deal, that!" Addi stated.

"It would have been, but the banks interfered again, making the administrator run another round of bidding."

"What happened?" I asked.

"We submitted roughly the same bid, but another company was nominated preferred bidder. The business was sold four weeks later to that company for about five percent of what we had offered."

"How does that make sense?" Tif questioned.

"It's anybody's guess!" Hawkshaw seemed ambivalent. "I think the administrators were prohibited from selling to the existing management."

"That's stupid!" Addi remarked.

"Yup, but you can't—" He was interrupted.

"—teach bankers!" Addi finished off his sentence.

"Thank you!" Hawkshaw smiled at him. "The insanity was led by one man. An Irish guy in his late forties. Medium height and build, a bit overweight, with a distinct band of blubber around his midriff."

"Ah, midlife spread that pays homage to the desk-ridden years of inactivity and gluttonous excess of corporate hospitality!" Tif smirked.

"He seemed inoffensive enough on first impression. But as time went on, I could see he was just a lying, weaselly little shit!"

"Don't hold back there, mate!" Tif quipped. "Let it all out!"

"You know it takes a lot to rile me, but he really was a detestable man who deserved to be flogged for self-adulation and the desire to hear his own voice!" We all laughed. "It didn't matter what I had said on the lead-up to administration, nor what I offered in commentary during administration, the potato-head only ever listened to answer, not to understand or learn. And his answers were always prefixed with the phrase, 'Let me be absolutely clear'."

"That would be irritating!" Addi supported.

"It was! Even more so because I knew in my head it meant he hadn't listened to a word I'd said, but was going to give his royal-ass opinion and decree!" Hawkshaw put on an Irish accent. "It has always bemused me that such individuals can be gifted the responsibility to play with other people's livelihoods and money, when they have such hubris."

"And makes you wonder how they got through the psychometric tests?" Tif kidded.

"That hubris isn't exclusive to banking, you know! I'm always coming across over-promoted people." Newt remarked. "Individuals who don't understand that the higher you ascend in an organisation, the more diverse the sphere of control, the less time there is to understand every element and the more you have to rely on discipline experts to abridge situations and provide advice-laden opinions."

"I bet they're all men?" Tif's sarcasm was self-evident.

"Actually no, it's a mixed bag! That's diversity kicking in. However, they had all stopped listening to the experts around them, thinking they could conjure the solution in ignorance." She clarified.

"Well, that was certainly true of my potato-head, lying, weaselly little shit!" Hawkshaw spat the words out. "His Dutch sidekick and this lady who dressed like a prostitute, who the administrator had appointed, made things worse!"

"You can't say that!" Newt shouted with disgust.

"I'm sorry, but you'd have said the same if you'd seen her! She was east European, I think, and wore these ridiculously tiny skirts that left little to the imagination! Her thighs were exposed nearly to the top and immodestly revealed far too much when she bent over a desk! Which she seemed to do excessively, oblivious to the peepshow she enacted..."

"A right 'three penny upright' then!"

"Might have known you'd know a phrase like that." Newt shook her head disapprovingly to Tif's reference to the Victorian phrase for a cheap up-against-the-wall prostitute.

"I doubt she'd have been cheap. She just loved the attention! All I saw was a pending sexual harassment case." He paused. "She came into my office one day after a meeting I'd had with the potato-head and explained at length that her company was there to help the employees through this difficult time. She said something like 'I know this is a tough time for you and I want you to know we're here to help. If you want, we have a counsellor who you can sit down with and talk about your feelings.'"

"Bet that went down well with you!" Addi kidded.

"Not really! I said something like, 'Sorry, I think you misunderstand. I'm not emotionally unstable, I am fucking pissed off!'" We all chuckled. "The conversation ended there. She rushed out of my office like she was being chased by a pack of rabid dogs!" He exhilarated.

"What about the Dutch dude?" Addi asked.

"He was like 'mini-me' to the Irish prick; except he was a smug twat as well! I went to give some information to one of his colleagues, once, and he was there, reclined in his seat, with his shoes up on the polished mahogany board table, grinning like he'd just lost his virginity. He looked at me and goes like, 'Hey, how's your day going?', to which I simply replied, 'Shit'. The funniest thing was that if you substituted the lone vowel in the banker's name for a 'u', it made a word that sounded like something Tif really enjoys!" He laughed and we all joined in. "The appointed administrator was a piece of work as well! Appointed by the court and still a lying scumbag that suckered the ass of his clients with the marketing mantra, 'That to err was human, but to err and not get caught was what they paid the high fees for'!"

"I'm afraid there are a lot of politicians like that." Newt remarked.

"Well, there shouldn't be!" Hawkshaw resounded adamantly. "These guys invalidated everything I had achieved across five years of my life. No one should have that power!"

I nodded, offering my support.

"I guess that is 'the way of the world'. People like my Irish and Dutch twats can affect your life for no reason whatsoever and never be held into account." Hawkshaw bitterly concluded.

"Such corruption has existed in banking for years! Remember Charles Ponzi, Bernard Madoff and Jérôme Kerviel?" Newt offered.

"Funny enough but I don't!" Tiff replied.

"Some say they have collectively defrauded over seventeen billion pounds! Complete walking detritus, if that's true! The worst of the worst! People like them are the reasons why capitalism gets a bad reputation from the masses as a philosophy to benefit the few on the backs of the majority!" Newt was fuming.

"It gets to you, doesn't it?" Tif smiled at her.

"Hawkshaw's got a name for them." I offered.

"Really?" Tif turned towards Hawkshaw. "Pray, do tell us what name you've invented for those immoral, greedy individuals!"

"Prosholes!" He proudly let out. "They are people who display unique and amalgamated characteristics of both a prostitute and an asshole. The prostitute being known to engage in paid-for sexual activity and the asshole being a stupid, irritating, and contemptible person."

"It is certainly unique!" Addi offered.

"And with a clear definition as well!"

"He's got a better definition than that!" I remarked. "Don't you have a poster printed with the definition on it in your office?"

Clearly happy with himself, Hawkshaw required little encouragement to offer the larger definition.

"Proshole, a negative adjective to describe a contemptable individual. Prosholes are frequently found working in business and aspire to ascend the ranks of an organisation in absence of morals and ethics. Prosholes are willing to oppress, mistreat, abuse and/or trample on others for enhanced remuneration. They are typically subversive, unscrupulous people, materially motivated, bearing no externally verifiable markings or attributes, who are proficient at concealment, and who will unashamedly reveal their true selves only when pushed into a corner or when such declaration will have no significant impact on their original objectives. Prosholes themselves have no verifiable gender bias or other defining demographic, and few, if any, redeeming features."

"That's pretty fucking comprehensive, mate!" Tif joked.

"What can I say? They're not my favourite people!" He grinned.

"I kind of think you're being a little soft there." Tif commented. "Sounds more like you abhor them!"

"The world is full of prosholes, so I just endeavour to identify them, avoid them and do my best." Hawkshaw replied. "Most of the time anyway." He gave a wink.

CONQUERING A MONOLITH

It wasn't so much the relaxed attitude with which Hawkshaw approached the world that made him admirable, as personified in his coining of the word 'proshole', but his underlying resilience and adaptability. To illustrate his point, on the day the power company was sold for a derisory sum, he hadn't simply gone quietly to the breach. Neither had he sat down and contemplated his navel. Instead of that, he had, within a week, issued a grievance against his new employer for constructive dismissal and bullying, presented subject access requests to the bankers to share any information they held in reference to him and created a joint venture technology company with an Australian partner he had been working with. As if this wasn't enough, he had also signed up to climb Mount Kilimanjaro for charity, grasping the opportunity presented by his 'employment void' to do something he had never done before.

These were the reasons why I admired Hawkshaw. Besides, his stories of the climb had captured my heart. His appetite to live in the moment and allow destiny to evolve was something I had always struggled to do. But we are all unique. Some people like the company of others, some don't. Some find it easy to make new friends, others feel socially awkward. While I was uncertain as to which group I fell into, Hawkshaw clearly belonged to the affable category. He could be left in the middle of the desert, make friends and sell sand. Which was fortunate because the group he had landed with in Tanzania was certainly very diverse.

Half the expedition had come from a London-based recruitment agency. The company's founder and chairman had decided to launch an internal competition for up to eight people to join him on what he had pitched to be the 'adventure of a lifetime'. It was both admirable and loyal teambuilding in the extreme. The remainder of the team consisted of a young, skinny male banker, a sturdy-framed farmer who was in the process of divorcing his wife, a vibrant, spiritual yoga teacher of African descent, a reserved logistics manager working in her dad's logistics business, a volatile red-head philosophy postgraduate completing her thesis—which title was *'Epistemic Normativity'*—a small Indian woman from Leeds working in tourism and who had confessed to joining the Mile High Club, a marketing executive, and Hawkshaw. Certainly not a group that would naturally congregate, but a group that offered an abundance of diversity to make their ascent enthralling nonetheless.

The trek would span across an entire week. Five days to ascend and two to descend. The bi-directional unequal itinerary was deliberate, designed to afford sufficient time during the ascension for everyone to get accustomed to the climate and increase their chances of reaching their objective without succumbing to altitude sickness. Mount Kilimanjaro's highest point, Uhuru Peak, sat five thousand eight-hundred and ninety-five metres above sea level. A giant monolith residing like an uninvited guest amidst the vast surrounding plains. At this altitude, the density of the air thins, barely capable of supplying eighty percent of the body's oxygen needs, leaving the body to compensate by breathing faster and deeper to balance the deficit. For those who failed to acclimatise, acute mountain sickness awaited them, and with it, the sole treatment of a rapid descent. Mount Kilimanjaro had more than its fair share of mountain sickness victims, since the final ascent takes adventurers up a thousand metres in elevation in about nine hours.

Hawkshaw had never done anything like that before and had set out on the trip in high spirits, excited by the unknown. As the trek progressed upward though, he had begun to question his decision. On the evening of day three, they had arrived in camp at an altitude of four thousand metres. They would remain at that level for two nights to adjust. But on the final run in to Mawenzi Tarn Camp that third night, Hawkshaw had fallen ill. Weakness, temperature, sore muscles and uncontrollable shivers. None of the symptoms were typical of altitude sickness, so he said nothing. Instead, going straight to his tent, he had undressed down to his thermal underwear and slipped inside his sleeping bag. Hawkshaw's silence didn't inhibit his canvas's companion, the farmer, from immediately going to get the team doctor, who arrived in a mild fluster. Systematic in his methodology of assessment, the doctor had completed his examination and determined, like Hawkshaw, that the condition wasn't altitude sickness. That said, his symptoms still led to a significant affliction of some sort. Nothing had been mentioned to Hawkshaw, and he had been given a high dose of paracetamol to suppress his fever, which he'd taken willingly before going to sleep.

Twelve hours of undisturbed slumber had made all the difference. He'd awoken the next day, fully revived and ready for action. Fever gone and appetite returned, the doctor was stunned. It was only then, over breakfast, that the withheld prognosis of malaria had been revealed and, with it, a recommendation for urgent care if symptoms had persisted. It was a relief for all that this decision had no longer been required. The next two days had been uneventful and visually unspectacular. Bulbous clouds descended to obscure the view and dispense an inch-thick snow cap that transformed the ragged landscape. When they made the final climb up to the school hut at Kibo Camp, they had traversed the grey barren shoulder between Mawenzi Peak and the base of Kibo. The walk had been sluggish, many of the team starting to feel the stifling impact of altitude, as they broke the four and a half thousand metre barrier.

On the night of the final ascent, completely revitalised from his twelve-hour bug, Hawkshaw had assembled with the team at midnight. Kilimanjaro was a dormant volcano and the peak's coned side was comprised of volcanic scree. A dusting of residue from historical activity. In the dark night sky, the temperatures plummeted, freezing the scree into a stable structure, solid enough to walk on. It was only in these early morning conditions that further ascent was generally attempted. The night sky was clear and wondrously black. Unaffected by the presence of artificial lighting, Hawkshaw had waxed lyrical about how the brilliance of the constellations had been mesmerising, how he had gazed up and counted the microscopic shards of light radiating from stars over four light years away. It was in those moments that Hawkshaw had discovered an expanded appreciation for the Earth's insignificance amidst the vastness of the universe. To travel to the nearest star would take over a hundred and thirty-seven thousand years. To lend perspective to that fact, the shards of radiance his eyes absorbed had commenced their journey at the end of the last ice-age.

As the final members of the expedition congregated, the lead guide completed a head count before setting off. Headlamps bowed to the ground, the speckled procession began its steep journey to the crater rim. Zigzagging from side to side, the vertical ascent was restrained, but couldn't mitigate the ever-intensifying physiological effects. Conversations gradually waned until silence engulfed the mountainside. An unnerving quiet, broken only by the noise of feet trudging across the ever-loosening scree. As daylight drew closer, the black void of space softened to a deeper atmospheric blue. With dawn, headlamps were switched off and heads raised to ascertain their progress. But the remaining distance to the rim couldn't be discerned from the climbers' point of view. Hawkshaw had recounted these moments with the least affection, focusing solely on his next step and then the step after that, blindly following the person in front of him. His pulse had been racing harder and harder to compensate for the ever-dwindling air. At one point he had decided to count the beats, but after ascertaining that his heart was pumping at more than a hundred and eighty beats per minute, decided not to check again. It wasn't like he could ignore it, though. He could feel the almost-desperate pounding in his chest, but was mercifully absent of symptoms of altitude sickness, for which he had been very thankful. That said, he had confessed that he had wondered how much longer his heart could maintain its accelerating objection to the environment. Just as he was about to attempt conversation and air this concern with the doctor, the procession turned a corner and was greeted by a sign announcing their arrival at Gilman's Point, the lowest official summit point on the mountain. Turning slowly to face the world, the vista had been sensational: a wide, flat expanse around the mountain, sitting below fragmented clouds that swelled from the accumulation of morning dew. He could see the field structure through the hazy gaps. The browns, yellows and greens of agriculture creating a patchwork quilt. Above the clouds, the sun breached the horizon for the first time that day. Burnt orange embers bathed the distant clouds. It was ethereal and Hawkshaw had sat there gazing out in wonder, feeling privileged to have been led to such a place. Proud also to have conquered his own fear as well as one of nature's challenges.

Eventually, the group's awe subsided sufficiently for their guide to begin enquiring who wanted to trek around to Uhuru Peak, the highest point on the crater rim. Hawkshaw had told me once that while it may not have seemed like a big issue to traverse the crater rim up to Uhuru peak, the extended journey meant another three hours trekking before descent and would take him two hundred metres higher. He'd never confessed to the rest of our friends, but he'd seriously considered quitting right there. He was a challenger who had made it to the crater rim, made it to an official summit point, but even he, with all his courage, had to consider physical limitations. However, when the moment to make a decision arrived, a sort of practicality of a different nature became the driving determinant. It had taken five days to get here. He had ascended over three and a half thousand metres from the base, overcome an undiagnosed sickness to be sitting there with what could be a once-in-a-lifetime opportunity. How could he conceive of withdrawing from the endeavour when the potential of further success remained ahead? So he had taken his place amongst the diminished group of adventurers.

The walk around the rim had been surreal. Following the path around the crater's edge, the outward view became obscured by the jagged metamorphic parapet. However, the absence of the external panorama was countered by the frozen, desolate wasteland that occupied the crater. Imposing glacial structures were expected in the depths of the Antarctic but not in Africa. Brutal lattices of ice worthy of Superman's Arctic home. It was spellbinding and time passed in a dreamy fast-forward motion. Hawkshaw and his tent buddy had been the first to arrive at Uhuru Peak. As a result, they had the opportunity to take some individual pictures of each other in front of the sign before the rest of the team caught up.

Their celebration at the ultimate summit was brief though, their guide requesting they take pictures and begin the descent as soon as possible. His concern regarding the duration of the time spent in what is known as the 'extreme altitude zone' was evident. Which, in plain English, meant that the longer they remained, the greater the risk of biological impairment. Having already pondered his limitations at Gilman's Point, Hawkshaw required little urging. Although the achievement and the majestic views from the pinnacle were memorable, the most recalled moment from his journey was yet to come. For while the chilling night air had leant cohesion to the steep sides of the mountain, the African sun had been steadily delivering its heat for three hours by the time they came to descend. Meaning the once firm volcanic aggregate had transformed into a loose bed of homogeneous rubble. As soon as Hawkshaw would plant a foot on the surface, the ground would crumble beneath it. With the steep incline already matching the scree's angle of repose, the pressure of his weight resulted in the formation of a micro-slip plain, upon which his boot would involuntarily mobilise, surrendering his body to follow, else fall. The latter not being an attractive proposition at the top of a near-thousand-metre unconsolidated mass of rubble, he'd launched after his front foot, imbued with the spirit of preservation. He had initially endeavoured to retain a steady pace, but nature soon asserted its control over him, incrementally pushing him forward with each step. Momentum was continuously building and, with it, the strength and composure required to move his trailing leg forward increased with every passing metre. As he'd reached the lower section of the scree, nature had sporadically placed boulders in his path. Rocks that had lost their original footing and been carried down the same path as him, to lay in wait. This is where life got more interesting. Unable to slow down, he had had to judge when to push to the side with his footing and when to jump directly over. The former solution was problematic, the unconsolidated bedding making lateral movements tough. The whole scenario could have been the basis for the stage of a video game, only he didn't have multiple lives or the chance to pause or the opportunity to reset and start again. He had only one shot and gravity as his timekeeper.

The base of the cone finally arched out, providing a natural breaking apron. Looking back, Hawkshaw would have loved to declare it had been his quick wits, balance and agility that mastered the art of scree skiing. But the truth was that luck had probably played the greatest part. Despite having started the climb at midnight, their return to base camp was brief. Just enough time to catch an hour's sleep and a snack before continuing the descent to a camp below the high-altitude zone. He'd made it to the final camp around five o'clock that day, having trekked for seventeen hours. Most of the group had got ready for dinner, but Hawkshaw hit his sleeping bag and went out cold until the next morning. After breakfast the following day, they had presented their guides and porters with a tip. Following receipt of which, in gratitude, their Tanzanian support team had danced and sung to them. The remainder of the trek had not been sombre, but adrenaline had subsided after the high of attainment and, with its withdrawal, tiredness had started to kick in. The heavens had also opened for them as they'd passed through the lower rainforest and a ceaseless downpour so heavy that no waterproof barrier could keep the damp at bay was offered to them. Hawkshaw had been sodden by the time they arrived at the collection point, though his spirits had remained buoyant in awe of what he had accomplished.

The purpose of relaying this story isn't to place Hawkshaw on any pedestal. It was clear from the confession of his fear of mortality that he wasn't on an ego trip. However, it was equally obvious that he had a strong grasp of himself. An indubitable comfort in his own skin. A belligerence not to let others affect his life and aspirations. In the face of adversity, he'd kicked off a legal challenge to bring closure to the past, created a new venture to light his future, then disappeared to experience the world for ten days. When he returned from Africa, the material fortunes had been mixed. The legal challenge had eventually failed, but the joint venture had gone on to secure government funding to progress a demonstration programme for the licenced technology. One door shut and another one opened.

As I reflected on my friend's adventure, my mind returned to the present, considering all I had heard tonight. The lesson I was endeavouring to take from all the opinions I had received so far was that life didn't just happen without intervention. I had to contribute. I had to know what I wanted. I had to aspire to something, to be motivated. I had to be a better version of myself. Perhaps one of Newt's philosophies and structures was the answer. Whatever the mechanism, I had to start taking accountability to feel better.

Unpicking Behaviour

Despite momentary surges of information, Newt hadn't been doing as much of the talking as usual. Apart from her brief response to my suicidal confession and fuzzy logic commentary, she'd been mostly silent since she had tried to introduce Maslow's hierarchy of needs. I didn't believe her quietness was a result of feeling undermined by Tif's advocacy for promiscuity, but more an acceptance that she understood she was the odd one out in our group. Not just because of her gender, but also because of her thought process. I had always known structures were something she identified with. She liked to use them to build relationships and make decisions. She was never one for impetuosity or emotive decision-making. I also knew that it was for those same reasons that when she offered guidance, she could seem dry and uninspiring.

In comparison, when Hawkshaw spoke, he oozed confidence and drew us into vicariously experiencing the majesty of the world. When Addi talked, we were beguiled in admiration for the boundless compassion and love that he held towards his family and friends. As for Tif's contribution, it was his offering of scintillating, salacious and sordid tales that none of us would dare consider doing ourselves, which were nonetheless engrossing to hear.

Therefore, when Newt spoke, it always felt like she was the last presenter of the day at a conference, when the audience is beleaguered and consumed by thoughts of that first drink at the bar. No matter what she said or how she said it, we would watch her respectfully with glazed eyes while our minds wandered elsewhere. It was a predicament I knew she had long accepted, but which I believed still precipitated internal frustration.

"What are you thinking about?" I encouraged her to speak.

"You'll all laugh at me..."

"We won't!" Hawkshaw declared, and that seemed to be instantaneous comfort for her.

"Fine...I was thinking about how to explain Beck's cognitive triad, cognitive distortions and cognitive behavioural therapy in a way that might lead to a less anecdotal approach to supporting Ethan and presenting options for him to move forward..."

"Okay, I'm lost already!" Tif grinned.

"Then give her the chance to explain!" Hawkshaw cut him down. "You might even learn something!"

"I can't promise not to bore you. Theory is what it is and it's hard to make it exciting." She seemed uncharacteristically reluctant, but when Hawkshaw encouraged her to carry on, she bounced back to life. "Beck's cognitive triad, also known as the negative triad, is a cognitive therapeutic view of a person aligned to three elements. In other words, three perspectives that manifest to define a person's depression. For obvious reasons you can see why such a structure might lend itself to this evening's agenda..." She acknowledged the statements I'd already made which were infused by the negative triad. "The triad involves the automatic, spontaneous and seemingly uncontrollable negative thoughts people suffering from depression have associated to themselves, the world around them and the future."

"I'm already enthralled!" Tif jibed.

"Just listen!" Addi defended her this time. "At least she's heard and understood Ethan's expressions of worthlessness! Heard his declaration of despondency that no one sees value in him. And worst of all, she has witnessed his confession of defeat and inability to see a future!"

'I am the definitive triad reference case.' I thought to myself.

"Rather than just suggesting a physical distraction," Addi continued forcefully, "she is trying to offer something more useful!"

Tif raised his hands in defeat. "I'm not trying to belittle how he feels! In the old days though, when I was a child, the treatment for such despondency was to tell the blighted individual to 'get a backbone', 'grow a pair' or 'stop their bellyaching and whinging'!"

"We're not in a 1980s boarding school, life is a little different today!" Hawkshaw remarked.

"It is." Newt interjected. "Depression has been legitimised as a treatable illness and is no longer viewed as a marker of weakness."

"But don't you think the legitimisation of mental health, of depression, has gone too far?" Tif questioned assertively. "That we have reached a point at which it is being exploited by the savvy inept employee as a foundation for job protection? That mental health has become the latest tool to undermine business performance? And, as such, that it has become yet another minefield of 'political correctness' that injects fear into the hearts of every Human Resources manager?"

We were all stunned into silence by Tif's uncharacteristic intellectual observation.

"There will always be a minority seeking to exploit any opportunity." Newt responded placidly. "That doesn't mean we should allow the exception to prove the rule." She paused for further comment from Tif but he didn't snap back.

"Embedded in an appraisal of Ethan's state of mind, I think the clear signs of cognitive distortion that feed the triad are laid bare." She continued. "He has a propensity for selective abstraction and overgeneralisation, taking a single event and inferring wider-rooted conclusions in absence of other information."

Everyone looked at me as if they needed me to confirm what Newt had said. I obliged by nodding.

"There is evidence of both magnification and minimisation, respectively blowing the negatives up into behemoths of doom and belittling any event that gives cause for positive emotion, or jubilation." They looked at me again and I nodded. "There is a deep-seated personalisation which associates everything to a failing of Ethan's making. Then, from that abstract soup of self-loathing and derision comes a unique flavouring of arbitrary inference, where negative conclusions regarding the future are embraced, based on little to no facts, ever reinforcing his sense of despondency."

"Can I say you've lost me now?" Tif questioned.

"She says that it is as if Ethan was determined to be unhappy." Addi offered succinctly.

Newt was absolutely correct. She hadn't seen me smile or laugh over the recent months, and I knew she hadn't shaken the confession I had made to her alone six months ago: that every morning I would wake without conscious decision to the thought 'I am unhappy'.

Sitting there, pondering her thoughts, her expression appeared relaxed. I anticipated a clear structure had crystalised in her mind that could serve as the perfect case study for characterising me and framing a treatment. But I couldn't help considering that maybe she was overthinking it. Was it so important to focus on framing a diagnosis or should the imperative be to introduce solutions? Whether it be Tif's societal detachment, Hawkshaw's invigorating challenges or Addi's rose-tinted philosophy. After all, as with all fields of medicine, the development of a robust theory that supports diagnosis is always rapidly overtaken by treatment theory. I was certain Beck's cognitive triad would be no exception.

"Cognitive behavioural theory, or CBT, is the emerging and most recommended pathway for rehabilitation." Exclaimed Newt, answering the question we were all asking ourselves, including me.

"So what's that when it's at home?" Tif asked offhandedly.

"CBT is very action-orientated. It focuses on an individual's behaviour, feelings and thoughts. It helps provide each individual with methods to control their emotions and cope with situations." She explained. Then looking directly at Tif, she went on. "You and your parents might deride the methodology as 'touchy-feely-crap', but you'd probably be in denial. Your judgement would be impaired, most likely due to repressed or uncomfortable memories from when you were younger. Bravado has much to answer for in the world of mental health. Good and bad."

She smiled to herself, but I was the only one to notice. I interpreted her smile to be directed at Tif, an almost condescending smile acknowledging that, even though he denied it, he knew he might benefit from behavioural therapy as much as I would. Newt truly couldn't contain her thoughts.

"You might want to consider it for your own good, Tif. Give yourself something to help you step away from the sexual abuse and degradation you like to torture yourself with. To help you see that, when you recount your tales, you seem to separate yourself from your sexual persona. Which indicates a potentially borderline personality disorder." She paused. "But what do I know? I've already attempted to advise you tonight with little impact. And I know approaching anything for a second time with you is troublesome..."

She left it there and returned to being silent, while the conversation meandered on in her absence, migrating back to being nestled in a triangle between Tif's embellished tales, Hawkshaw's champion attitude and Addi's unyielding love. At least she had noticed that her dialogue had coaxed a smile from me.

ENGINEERING TEMPTATION

Newt had always been career-blessed, so it came as a wonder that she would empathise with my predicament as much as she did. It was also probably why she relied upon academic and philosophical models to frame situations and aid her navigation of them. In her work life, she had always left jobs on her own terms and only ever interviewed for jobs that she subsequently secured. Apart from failing her driving test four times, she had never really known rejection. She had therefore never completely experienced the nagging self-doubt that rejection invited.

Some people would look at her and say she had enjoyed the gift of positive discrimination, but so what. The world of man had enjoyed such control and discrimination for centuries, laying judgments down on what the patriarchy ignorantly referred to as the weaker sex. Weaker sex my ass! Newt's presence of mind could not be dismissed as weak. Resilient, yes. Assertive, yes. Confident, yes. But never weak. And her rhetoric tonight was no different. She witnessed, absorbed and offered structured commentary. As she would in her job. If there ever was any criticism to bestow on her, it was that her persistent reliance on models to explain the world could feel cold and callous. It wasn't how her advice was intended, but it was an unavoidable side-effect of a textbook narrative.

Despite me being the focal point this evening, I could see she also harboured concern for Tif and had already intimated as much. She'd listened at length to his approach for reconciling rejection, which was to find solace and comfort in meaningless liaisons with less-than-virtuous women. Even though she had acknowledged that the need for physical relationships was one of the foundation stones for happiness, she had previously confessed to me that a happy soul could not honestly thrive on a deviant diet alone. And after listening to her comments tonight, I could tell she thought the traits of addiction were blossoming in him.

In opposition to this, Tif presented himself as strong and in control, but it was undeniable that his acts in their very nature were selfish. He kept on claiming he was a considerate lover, and in the moment I thought he might well be, but no matter the tenderness in passion, the encounters could only ever be considered soulless. There was never any depth to the asserted desire. No real emotional connection was explained. Therefore, like Newt, I struggled to believe anyone could be so voluntarily cavalier despite evidence demonstrating they could.

Of greater concern to her, if that were possible, would be the knowledge I could actually see some allure to his lifestyle. Passing from one day to the next, never looking back once a moment had passed. Always hunting out the next high. Perpetually granting myself freedom from yesterday in search of the excitement of tomorrow. I could only imagine how liberating that might be. I was nowhere near as proficient as Newt at deconstructing people's behaviour, but even I had observed the escalation in Tif's thrill-seeking desires over time. His need to better every encounter with some new level of experience. And with that escalation in deviance, there was an inevitable increasing selfishness to those encounters. Seeking attainment of his expectations ahead of his temporary companions and in complete ignorance to those who cared about him. Like any other addiction, his behaviour was self-destructive.

And just like every addict, he seemed to choose to ignore the role it played on his shrinking soul. I couldn't help but think his short-sighted philosophy would leave him absent of any tangible life pursuits, only feeding further his slow descent into the dungeon of carnal servitude and correspondingly increasing self-loathing.

I could tell Newt desperately wanted to offer him guidance as well, although she seemed to know it would yield little benefit if such advice was unsolicited. Unfortunately, we all knew Tif would never ask. A trait not uncommon to addicts. Besides, seeking guidance required acknowledging the existence of a problem and Tif's morals never left room for introspection.

My judgment was possibly a little harsh because I had also observed mood swings and a flare of irritability once in a while. These uncharacteristically negative temperaments frequently coinciding with an absence of stories to tell; which I had determined to indicate a self-imposed abstinence. An attempt by Tif to correct his behaviour. Still, I had witnessed this behaviour several times and knew the cycle would repeat soon enough. Tif was just too weak, too immersed in his way of life to try and detach himself from it. I also believed there was a risk that if successful in maintaining sexual abstinence, he would expose himself to a void of free time so large that he would be even more disoriented. Which was why I assumed Newt had chosen to accept her incapacity to change Tif. She had told me that because of that, she worried about his long-term influence over me. He had after all been one of my longest standing friends and she confessed it had become clear to her that, in our younger years, that bond had been so strong nothing could break it now. It was because of this connection that I understood she focused on marginalising his influence instead. A battle she had admitted to being concerned of losing, having seen a glint of interest flicker from me and, surprisingly, Addi, several times over the past few months. She told me she didn't know how deep that interest actually went for either of us, but stressed that any adoption of Tif's philosophy, regardless of how far it went, would likely be the last straw for me, the last blow that could break me.

With regards to Addi, she admitted she was less certain of the consequences. She just feared any step towards adultery would foster a breeding ground for so much guilt that his caring soul would be overcome and all that was good in his life would be destroyed. She was probably right. Addi prided himself of being selfless in his care and consideration of others. Who knew what would happen if that purity became contaminated with remorse?

COMPENSATING FLAWS

"You know, the longer the evening goes on, the more I identify flaws in each of us." Newt looked around the table. "And the more I acknowledge an overlap in our attributes."

"What do you mean?" Addi frowned.

"Well, we've got Ethan, who is the depressive, wrestling daily to find purpose, and in absence of that, has forged an addictive coping mechanism with alcohol. Which has started to degrade his body."

"Yes, not good mate." Tif remarked.

"Then we have Tif." She continued. "Also an addict, but steeped in testosterone, which erodes his soul and mental stability. No matter how much he may choose to deny it, he is caught in a destructive spiral, his increasing depravity driven by a need to feel wanted, in ignorance of the love that awaits him at home."

Tif objected, but Hawkshaw stepped in to defend Newt.

"Which leads us to Addi. Perpetually on cloud nine, embracing the love that overflows within his family, to the neglect of all else."

"Surely that's a good thing?" Addi questioned.

"Yes, although your life's purpose is now crafted by a primary desire to please them; which obviates your ability to maintain structure in your own life. You persistently place their needs ahead of your own, all in the name of love."

"Again, is that not a good thing?" Addi was struggling to see the flaw she was alluding to.

"Maybe. I would bet it has left you exposed to brief moments of frustration though. When the effort you've surrendered for the happiness of others is treated with entitlement..." She paused for effect. "I bet in those moments you feel frustrated. Maybe even angry?"

Addi remained silent. As if by being silent he lent no credibility to the statement. I could see him fidgeting with his wedding band under the table though, revealing how close to the truth Newt had actually struck.

"What about you then?" Tif challenged.

"Fair enough. I am a person who is lucky to feel the unwavering, unconditional love of my husband. Which enables me to aspire in my own endeavours with the confidence that he is always behind." She started.

"So you're basically married to Addi." Tif was met by her stern gaze.

"Yes, I receive the equivalent love and affection from my husband that Addi offers to his family. It is that love which allows me to embrace structures to navigate my own path with confidence and without distraction."

"And your flaw is...?" Tif prompted her to complete the analysis of herself.

"I don't reciprocate as much as I could or probably should." She confessed.

"And me?" Hawkshaw waited patiently for his big reveal.

"Yes, last but certainly not least, there is you. You make structures to suit your pursuits. While I adapt models to discover ways to progress, you see the goal and establish your own framework to lead you there. Your conviction is so resolute that you can captivate others into rapidly aligning with your objectives. You are the type of person I fear the most at work. Someone who can inspire solely based on the tenuous foundations of your own beliefs. The type of personality that could lead a revolution if they desired. Quick-tongued. Quick-witted. Quick to engage. All attributes of a powerful leader."

"I don't see a problem there!" Hawkshaw remarked.

"So let me ask you one question." She took a sharp breath. "Do you ever think you are wrong? Do you ever think you make mistakes?"

Her questions shocked him into silence.

"Wow dear! Looks like you've got all bases covered with that analysis!" Tif remarked antagonistically. "Tell me, when you set out tonight, were you aiming at alienating everyone?"

"I don't know, she's pretty accurate about me." Hawkshaw pronounced. "My approach is that life is tough and is over in a blink, so I choose to never forget that it's me who decides what I get from it. I can't waste a moment. If that comes over as Newt describes, I accept it, but make no apologies."

"Amen to that!" Tif supported. "Don't waste a moment! That's something I can endorse!"

"I don't mean the way you're approaching it." Hawkshaw reproached. "I mean live every moment without remorse for what you could have done. I've never been depressed, but I know if I ever were, I would regret more wasting away a day without action than whatever would have driven me down to begin with." Newt agreed. "Flaws of our past selves aside, the future is the only thing that can be changed." He continued. "There's nothing any of us can do about yesterday. I know that sounds a little brutal, but it's true."

"You just need to build yourself back up! Focus on what you have, on the fundamental needs that you already have in your life! Hold on to those basic elements and build on them." Newt offered further comment, invigored by Hawkshaw's response to her criticism.

"I may have missed some of the earlier conversation, but don't overthink things. I've always found that if I just focus on what I want to do, strive for who I want to be, the rest just takes care of itself. The things that aren't required to deliver that future state become unimportant and stop sucking energy away from the objective."

"I kind of support that." Addi remarked. "And don't forget, you've got a hell of a wife who loves you and will be there for you no matter what!" Addi addressed me directly.

"The more we talk, the more I see the overlap of personalities! Each of us embodies a discrete self-improvement persona." Newt asserted.

"And here we go again!" Tif taunted.

"Ignore him! Carry on, please." I asked.

"Thank you, I will." She smiled at me. "There are six acknowledged self-improvement personalities. Three are based on the attributes of the *reformer*. Individuals who like to drive internal change inside an acknowledged social order. That is definitely Addi and myself. We are neither static nor the type to deconstruct and rebuild a ship while crossing the Atlantic." She inhaled deeply, as though readying herself for a long and complex explanation. "The other three personas are based on the attributes of the *disruptor*. They push for change outside of the social order. Some might argue disrupters are anarchists, insurrectionists, or militants. Tif and Hawkshaw definitely fall into the disruptor band, without being extremists. They are conformists who are open to question and interrogate society's doctrines."

"And me?" I asked.

"Then there is you. The one trapped in an identity crisis, struggling to decide whether you are a reformer or a disruptor."

"Is that it?" Tif didn't wait for a response. "Thank God!"

"No, there's more! You are what is known as the *hacker*. Hackers are habit-orientated disruptors. They get lost in chaos and willingly break things just to feel like they are doing something. I think we can all agree this certainly characterises what you are doing through your adulterous lifestyle."

"She's got you sussed!" Addi joked.

"As for you," she looked at Addi, "you're what's known as a *holy warrior*. You are a value-orientated reformer. You like to figure out what to do with broken things rather than discard them. For you, there is always something to be done, that can be delivered compassionately, to overcome any situation. This is what you believe in."

"She's got you pegged an' all!" Tif quipped snidely.

"While your value system is admirable and your unbounding love for all is commendable, it does also serve to marginalise you, because you can be prone to being absorbed in your attempt to save lost causes."

179

"Here's a lesson for you, Ethan! Start worrying if Addi tries to fix you!" Tif joked childishly. We all ignored him.

"I'm a pure *investigator*, and proud of it! I am a process-oriented reformer who likes to dive into problems to understand the core issues. I enjoy unearthing what has actually caused the problem. 'Treat the cause, not the symptom' is my mantra. It's why I am so focused on the architecture of Maslow's hierarchy, because it provides a foundation for both diagnosis and treatment building."

"Yup, but sometimes life is too random to be modelled." Hawkshaw declared.

"Maybe, but I'm happy to play with the law of averages that supports the models rather than be cavalier!"

"Fair enough! If you think probability is the best companion for a happy life." Hawkshaw dismissed her back. "What's my unique profile, then?"

"To be honest, I'm struggling to find your perfect match. You're like a chameleon, switching between two personas." Hawkshaw smiled with delight at her comment. "Which isn't that surprising when I accept your dogged refusal to conform to type in any situation. On the one hand, you act as a *contrarian*, a goal-oriented disruptor who pushes for change and fights to prove the future state is better than the status quo. Glimpses of this can be clearly witnessed in your career: you're always aspiring to deliver the most challenging and unprecedented ventures, fighting and justifying causes before the masses even acknowledge the problem."

"Sounds pretty good to me!" Hawkshaw received the classification with pride.

"Ah, but the rest of the time you are a *legalist*. A value-based disruptor who believes a broken system can be revitalised and made beautiful again. In this regard, your character is steeped in traditionalism. You believe in mutual respect and the freedom of speech. But you also respect the sanctity of marriage, the right to be proud of your national heritage without being branded a nationalist, and the right to openly celebrate Christmas, not out of disrespect to minority ethnics, but as a custom of the indigenous culture which settled in this country across the centuries."

"Still pretty happy with that!" Hawkshaw sat back in his seat with a big smile.

"To an outsider, we are an unlikely bunch of personalities. Unlikely to be friends."

"Love you too!" Tif remarked dismissively.

"Don't misinterpret me, I love all of you! Even you, Tif. But the unyielding positions that each of us bring to the table inevitably leads to heated debates, which could be viewed as arguments from an outsider's viewpoint. Still, for us, no matter how great the perceived impasse, we never falter in staying together to find a way forward. We have a strange and dysfunctional bond which somehow seems always to survive to fight another day. Each of us contributes to our ideas."

"I agree!" I said. "However, if we take a step back, it seems apparent to me that Hawkshaw's strength of character is the glue that holds us together!"

DISCOVERING BOUNDARIES

As Newt had implied, Hawkshaw was our collective's glue and, for now, the furthest removed from my present state of mind out of all of them. With his infinite opportunities, he was the adventurer. The entrepreneur. The finisher who saw through a challenge to the end just for the satisfaction of accomplishing it. Both he and Newt sought to overcome obstacles, but where Newt was methodical and practical in her approaches, Hawkshaw was simply fuelled by instinct, passionate vision and clinical interpretation of the situations he faced. If there was any flaw to be witnessed, it was that his passion sometimes meant passengers on his journey had to deal with scant explanations in order to meet his timetable for delivery.

"Compared to Tif, where he fails to establish personal goals that would aid his emotional growth, I have so many things I want to accomplish that at times it feels like life may be too short. I pursue everything with vigour and my bucket list is endless." Hawkshaw declared.

"Nothing like blowing your own trumpet!" Tif snidely commented.

"If there's a shortcoming to my approach to savouring life, it is that I occasionally need reminding that I am not devoid of limits." He replied.

"We all have boundaries, mate." Addi comforted.

"Yes, but I seem to find mine when actually passing beyond them." Hawkshaw drew in a deep breath. "Like when I canoed down the Zambezi River!"

"Here we go again!" Tif moaned, tiring of the Hawkshaw show. No one paid any attention.

"Wasn't that the charity thing you did a couple of years ago?" Newt asked.

"Yes! I signed up to paddle just over a hundred kilometres along the river in small two-people inflatable canoes. It was gruelling, but I'd prepared myself for that. However, what I had underestimated was my mental approach to the potential of an encounter with not-so-friendly animals. Specifically, the danger indigenous wildlife posed. I had completely overlooked that!"

"A bit stupid, given that hippos and crocodiles are well-established cohabitants of the Zambezi River!" Newt seemed surprised of Hawkshaw. "It's well-known that their behaviour and preferred areas of residency are keenly observed and mapped out by the rangers who vigilantly patrol the national park to protect them from poachers."

"Yes, so 'well-known'!" Tif kidded. We all ignored him again.

"Apparently, the rangers are like human guardians of nature who know how to spot danger and avoid contact." Hawkshaw resumed the storytelling. "But as with every living thing, they don't always conform to the type. That is what happened one day as we drifted downstream."

"I recall you telling me this!" Newt interrupted him enthusiastically. "You were floating in single file towards a gentle set of rapids. It was an area where water flowed quickly, in contrast to where hippos generally liked to bathe. A lone hippo emerged with gaping mouth from the water. It clasped its teeth tight on the side of one of your canoes, angrily thrashing its head, the canoeists aboard fleeing to nearby boats, leaving the hippo to shake off the deflating and abandoned canoe lodged between its teeth."

"Very descriptive!" Tif raised his eyebrows dismissively.

"And to avoid further assault, the rest of us were led into evasive manoeuvres by the two lead guides, while the third guiding canoe, which was occupied by the park ranger, took position with his rifle, readying himself to discharge warning shots or, if required, directly aim at the beast." Hawkshaw emulated Newt's enthusiasm, narrating the tale a little like a game hunter.

Tif took over with mocking gusto, as if doing the voice over to a wildlife programme. "It was at this moment Hawkshaw's bravado had been introduced to the boundaries of mortality. As he arced his paddle rapidly from side to side, in perfect unison with his boat buddy, a vicar no less, the hippo resurfaced alongside them. Catching its head in the corner of his eye, Hawkshaw watched his paddle disappear into the water and sweep back, narrowly missing the creature's mouth as he drew the blade out again. There had been no time for panic or exclamation, just for methodical, repetitive, precision strokes to propel the canoe away. Like a track athlete, the explorer didn't look back, for fear that it may concede precious millimetres of safety. He just worked his muscles hard to drive them through the rapids and to the sanctuary of a riverbank downstream." He laughed. "I've heard the story before as well!"

"What about you two?" Hawkshaw looked at Addi and I. We shook our heads.

"Well, then I'll finish the story!" He looked down on Tif. "Before I'd left for Zambia, animal attacks had been a low-ranking probability I'd dismissed. But after witnessing the ferocity of the attack and coming within inches of a hippo's gaping jaw, my perspectives changed. Adventure is good, but life is essential. And although the event hasn't significantly altered my appetite for experiences, it definitely taught me a valuable lesson in personal due diligence."

I listened to the story, as I had done with everyone's tales tonight, inevitably comparing myself to them. In this instance, I was consumed with doubt and fear. Hawkshaw was self-assured and exuded panache with every act and word, whereas I was reserved from lacklustre results of all my recent endeavours. He absorbed lessons from every failure and moved forward to the next opportunity seemingly unperturbed, greeting each sunrise with an audacious 'You haven't seen the best of me', whereas I began each day with the apathetic 'Here we go again'. Hawkshaw was incapable of sitting still. Every second of life mattered to him. Time passed without action was wasted time. In truth, his energetic disposition was an unrealistic expectation, but one Hawkshaw refused to concede to. His very heart had to be in pursuit of something meaningful. Life had a singularity that needed to be nourished and cherished. And he would push his physical and mental limits until his body enforced retirement.

The only friend in our group where Hawkshaw failed to provide an antidote or counterpoint to their core character was Addi. That was because no one wanted or needed to be the opposite of loving. Addi's compassion, support, understanding and caring of his family and friends, wrapped in a selfless love, offered no cause for criticism, just admiration. Hawkshaw had once confessed to me that he had pondered the potential that existed if he and Addi could collaborate. His desire to yield change, to make a difference, crafted by Addi's infinite compassion and belief in the good of humanity. I had concurred they could become a force to be reckoned with. And while such collaboration had come close to being realised several times, external forces had always conspired to derail the partnership. Hawkshaw told me he refused to give up, though. Opportunities would always come and go. He knew that, in time, the future would present an avenue for them to unite for good. Until then, he would remain vigilant to see the chance before it arrived.

While each of these character differences was part of what set Hawkshaw apart from each of us, his blind refusal to see limitations was what made him unique. He nurtured a desire for improvement. A relentlessness for perpetual growth. Some people might have said it was his addiction. To be honest, it would be a reasonable assertion. Hippos aside, his addiction harmed no one, including himself. So if there was such a thing as a perfect vice, perhaps this was it.

One event captured this resoluteness more than any other and it wasn't climbing a mountain or abseiling off a bridge. It hadn't taken a few minutes or a couple of weeks to complete, but four years. It was an event that unequivocally demonstrated his dogged belligerence not to be defined. To not become a stereotype of any kind. He had written a novel. A work of fiction that he had conjured up on a flight from Heathrow to Vancouver. In the ten hours it had taken to travel halfway around the globe, he had scribbled a ten-page synopsis of the story. A story that was so clear in his head from inception. It had only took him a year from that day to complete a manuscript he was satisfied with. Then had come the challenge of finding a publisher. Letters and opening chapters were circulated to every publishing house and agent he could find that would accept unsolicited manuscripts from debut authors.

Rejection letters came in one after the other, some polite, some less so. But he continued nonetheless, galvanising himself with the advice that he only needed to find one person who saw the promise in his vision.

Then it happened. A letter had arrived from a boutique publishing house, inviting him to a meeting at their office. He had attended, ready to convince them of the commercial proposition his work represented, but they had required no such guidance. They were there to deal and an offer had been presented almost immediately. Hawkshaw had been momentarily flummoxed, but quickly composed himself. The dialogue had been positive. Marketing. Print volumes. Future rights to works. But then the killer blow, the book was too long. It required culling by at least a quarter. The story operated across five main characters and two different time frames, with continuity links between the present and the past abound. Every paragraph removed or edited held consequences and eroded the flow of suspense. However, the requirement to reduce the novel size was a condition precedent on the tabled offer and he could only accept it.

Another year passed before his new version of the story emerged. In practical terms, he had written the book again. Such was his tenacity to complete the challenge he had embarked on, he had accepted the tortuous task with relish, unpicking each chapter, word for word, and recomposing the narrative more succinctly. His publisher had been largely supportive of the process. The only disagreement they had had was over an explicit sex scene Hawkshaw had retained, which they considered superfluous. For him though, it was a defining event to crystallise the darkness that consumed his villain. In the end, the publishers had conceded and the scene survived the final edit.

Some individuals may still be wondering what the big deal was. For that, all I can offer is the consideration of such an undertaking while in full-time employment, completing an MBA and having just become a new parent. Armed with that knowledge, most people appreciated the endeavour must have consumed every spare moment he could conjure. As I've said, dogged, tenacious, relentless, reaching. Love him or loath him, that was Hawkshaw.

Escaping the Drama

"I know it seems impossible, but you need to stop playing the victim, Ethan." Hawkshaw cut to the chase. "The world is overrun with victims and one thing is for certain, no one really cares. Because no matter how good friends they may be, there comes a point when it just feels too damn hard to maintain support."

"That's almost like a bully's mentality!" Newt exclaimed.

"Be that as it may, but it's not intended that way!" Hawkshaw responded. "There just comes a time when you need to find peace, healing and happiness for yourself!"

Overheard from across the bar, Hawkshaw's unsympathetic rhetoric could have been misconstrued as persecution. But it wasn't. Hawkshaw was honest and genuine in his thoughts. He could see me finding comfort from playing the victim, which wasn't uncommon. When a person felt persecuted or oppressed, it could be justified or soothing to blame others for misfortune. To level the anxiety and anger at the feet of another. There's a release that comes from that. A contentment from assigning blame. Especially when such assignment may be legitimate. To some extent, though there's a period beyond which such projection of fault becomes invalid, and the victim is using the circumstance as an excuse for maintaining the status quo. I felt from his increasingly unsympathetic expression that this was where Hawkshaw feared I had arrived and he needed me to know my right to pity was nearly expended.

"I know this is a stupid example, but I spent a year trying to find an agent or a publisher who saw my novel the way I did." He smirked with reflection. "You wouldn't believe the number of rejection letters I received. Nearly one hundred. All with one of three explanations. Either they were a small agency and had to be selective with the manuscripts they sought to publish, or the current market and economic climate was challenging for the industry, so they needed to focus on projects they felt best placed to support. My personal favourite, though, was that they were just not on my 'wavelength'!"

"Nobody said that!" Tif challenged.

"They did! Frankly, that's the most hurtful, because it feels like a judgement on a work that defined a year of my life. Everyone says, 'don't take it personally', but that's impossible. When you are unsuccessful, it is because someone doesn't like what you have to offer enough. It's that simple. And its inescapable."

"Cheery thoughts..." Tif retorted.

"It's not about being cheery! It's about being realistic." Hawkshaw paused. "When you write a book, the first piece of advice most authors would give is to write because you like it. Write for yourself. At least that way, when you are finished, one person is guaranteed to be happy. The rest is chance. A chance it lands on someone's desk when they are willing to read, are emotionally in a good place and actually appreciate what you have to offer enough to fight their peers to accept you as a client. That's how life works in general! Having ideas that you can convince others hold value."

"And when they don't?" Tif queried.

"Then have the strength to see it simply as the wrong person or the wrong day, and move on."

"Like most suggestions offered tonight, easier said than done!" Newt defended compassionately.

"When you say things like that, Newt, all you do is feed the sickness!" He asserted. "When it comes down to it, like me looking for an agent or publisher, you have to armour yourself to take the knocks and keep chasing dreams."

"You do know when you talk like that, you become one of the persecutors?" Newt proposed.

"You're wrong!" Hawkshaw proclaimed. "Sounding like you for a moment, I'm a *challenger*. Whereas you want to be a coach, but fall short, presenting yourself instead as the *rescuer*, who does little but reinforce the *victim*'s basis for anxiety."

"What the hell are you on about?" Tif questioned, confused.

Hawkshaw was playing Newt at her own game. Using terminology from two well-established social models that have been used to explain the roles individuals play in conflict environments, and which he knew she would be familiar with. One model representing the negative situation, the other its positive reflection.

"It strikes me that we are wallowing around the Karpman drama triangle!" Hawkshaw announced to a stunned Newt. "Ethan sits at the top, playing the *victim*. Removed from reality, feeling hopeless, ashamed and incapable. He uses Newt as his *rescuer*, a crutch who validates how he feels and offers structure and justification. Despite being well-intentioned, she isn't always equipped or strong enough to get him to adopt one of the structures to elevate himself from this slump, because she fears the consequences of removing her sympathy. However, her role is much more complex than that. I'll explain in a moment."

Around the table, everyone looked confused by Hawkshaw's sudden turn of words.

"Tif, though he doesn't see it, he is a *persecutor*. He wouldn't bully Ethan, but through his advocacy for meaningless sex as a vent for frustration, he inadvertently seeks to set him up for greater guilt and self-persecution. In some ways, he is the worst of tormentors because he veils himself with selflessness and is blissfully ignorant to the real role he plays."

"Ouch!" Addi was stunned by Hawkshaw's direct condemnation.

"Addi and I aren't represented in the triangle."

"Shocker!" Tif commented petulantly.

"That's because we offer little by way of negative schema into the group. Instead, I think we offer the positive reflection of all that the three of you represent."

Tif shook his head in disbelief at the arrogance. Hawkshaw continued.

"As opposed to Tif, I am the *challenger*. With my can-do attitude, I both consciously and unconsciously provoke action. I actually demand it."

"Can you say 'egocentric'?"

"My role doesn't end there, because I also purvey the qualities of a *creator*. As a survivor and thriver, I advocate setting a vision and focusing on its delivery. Continually tasking and stretching myself."

"You seem to have your strengths and limitations sorted," Tif couldn't take it anymore, "although I'm not hearing you confess to many of the latter!"

194

"That's because, for me, limitations are just excuses for failure, which shouldn't be accepted except in extreme circumstances; like with my hippo."

"So what's Addi?" Newt probed, allegedly curious to test the full extent of his knowledge, while appearing both excited and angry at the sudden depth of comprehension he was demonstrating.

"Addi is a *creator* as well, but a selective one. All he aspires to create is the perfect family. I don't mean the picture-perfect postcard version. It doesn't matter to him how the outside world sees them. It only matters how each member of his family feels about themselves and each other. He wants them to feel loved, to feel supported and to feel the joy life offers. His goal is singular, but that doesn't make him any less a creator or any less successful at it." Hawkshaw complimented.

"And you have me as a *rescuer*?" Newt quizzed.

"Not just a rescuer! You are a chameleon of positive and negative effects. I know it would be an injustice to classify you solely by your impact within the confines of a drama, because your intention is good. When your approach breaks through into the other person's psyche, you are the best of *coaches*, that is, the polar opposite of a *rescuer*." He smiled at her. "That's why you are so successful in your career. In fact, that is a defining criteria which characterises your role. You have empathy and, although you can clearly detach yourself from personal relationships, you comfortably stay true to your desire to help and mentor. In your private life, where personal histories increasingly cloud relationships and emotions, your empathy veers towards sympathy and that is what occasionally constrains your effectiveness in personal interactions.

"Tonight though, you have been as objective and sharp as ever. You know Ethan needs a structure to hold on to and build from. You know he needs a way to frame his circumstance and life, a way which offers both explanation and focus for growth. In our wider group, you know Addi is being drawn to the exhilaration of detachment that Tif's life portrays. And you realise it is a credible risk that he may fail to remain true to his family."

Our whole group looked stunned by that assertion. Especially Newt. But Hawkshaw had bigger claims to make.

"Then there is Tif. An addict torn by desire. In denial of how conflicted he really is. A mess that needs help as much as Ethan does. Albeit there have been glimpses recently of an awakening in him. His character is less buoyant and brash than it used to be. Not deflated as such, but less edgy."

Hawkshaw held nothing back. Once again this evening, one of my friends had stunned our group into silence.

COLD AWAKENING

I was surprised by Hawkshaw's observations concerning Tif. I thought I had been the only one to see the glimpses of morality he had alluded to. Recently, Tif had appeared increasingly tired of regaling us with stories of his adventures, looking weary of supporting us in finding a little dark excitement, of finding a spirit of unconventionality in our lives, allowing us to live unconfessed desires through him. To live vicariously in his exploits. It was as if his youthful testosterone was desiccating and he had begun to question the motivation for his sexual deviance. The dilemma had probably been a long time in the making, suppressed inside it had evolved ready to be released one day as a dawning awareness of spent desire, manifesting like an inventor's idea. A realisation that the passion and lust for nocturnal intimacy which had characterised his life so far may be nearing an end.

His proclivity for discovering and exploring mutually beneficial intimate interactions had been a foundation stone for his psychology. Whereas tonight he still appeared confident in his storytelling, he had previously admitted that the bravado was skin-deep, cloaking his underlying insecurity. The truth was that his lust for carnal pleasure was a form of therapy, a way to feel strength and success in a world that conspired to thwart him at every turn. He may not be able to live the glorious life of his social media friends, but he had secrets and experiences they couldn't imagine. It was something he could fall back on, a core competence he considered made him worthier and elevated his spirits. A sort of right for self-adulation.

The truth was Newt had been correct when she suggested this core competence had become an addiction. An addiction so tightly aligned to his every breath that he dragged an imaginary, intravenous stand everywhere with him. An addiction that he had used for years to disguise the truth about how he felt about himself. That he despised himself. It was with such acknowledgement that the greatest of life's falls were delivered. And it was on that cerebral cliff edge that Tif had recently stood, anticipating the drop.

The path to the precipice hadn't been long. He had been walking a parallel course to it for a long time. But it had taken a unique set of circumstances for him to identify the looming edge and to feel the increasingly friable foundation of his sanity start to crumble. These unique circumstances had taken the form of five developments which had almost simultaneously rushed to help him see clearly. It was only when he had stepped back to consider them for a second one afternoon, sitting in Starbucks drinking coffee, that he had realised the ludicrous nature of his situation, and the absurdity of him.

The first development had been associated to a lady he had met online. It had been the most peculiar relationship in its evolution. Tif had responded to an advert for a married couple who were looking for another couple or another woman. There was no mention of men, but Tif had discovered sometimes that, when pushing a wagon uphill, there was less competition from would-be suiters willing to exert the effort and, occasionally, someone stepped down from the brow to help pull the wagon to the top. He'd conversed and met with several lesbians with this approach, and this had been another successful instance. However, it would have been reasonable to say that while a hand had been extended towards him, the journey to the crest had been steady and frustrating because of innumerable false peaks.

The couple lived close by, within the unofficial thirty-minute travel perimeter that seemed to be established as a decision metric in the swinging world. They were British, with Pakistani heritage. Tif had always been cautious at the beginning of any new connection. With each acquired piece of information, he would assimilate it into an evolving profile of his correspondent. Usually, the early-stage dialogues were protracted and protected within the secured environment of the community website, but occasionally, when things got serious, the discussion would move beyond those confines to more personal platforms.

Email addresses had been exchanged in this instance and the dialogue resumed without the background noise of other adversaries. For this world of deceit, the email address for his correspondent was unusually real. He could actually Google her and find pictures of a human being that remarkably matched the pictures on her profile. Now, if it had been the same picture as her profile picture, his *phoney alert* alarm bells may have rung, but it hadn't been. Just another picture of the same woman. And with those on her profile reflecting personal and social occasions at restaurant tables and by swimming pools, he had no reason to doubt his findings. Still, the alarm bells had rung. Even as the metallic throng increased to a deafening cacophony in an attempt to alarm him to the perceived danger of his current course, an equal rush of excitement had consumed him and hastened his heart. He was conflicted, but hooked.

This internal battle of desire versus foreboding wasn't due to a state of celebrity on behalf of his correspondent; though there was notoriety. It wasn't due to her unparalleled beauty either. No, the opposing sentiments that consumed Tif were due to the mugshot he had found himself staring at. She was dressed in a typical prison-service blue sweatshirt. Her shoulder-length dark brown hair, unkept and draped loosely over her shoulders. Head slightly cocked to one side, skin unblemished, nose straight and long, eyes flat and sad portraying a blend of confusion, disbelief and acceptance. With her headshot presented alongside her co-defendants, she failed to look the part for which she was accused. She looked out of place. She had been arrested in a public case and sentenced to six years in prison upon a charge for drug trafficking. Now, many people may have run a mile at this sudden discovery, like his head had been trying to convince him, but Tif had resisted conceding to premature condemnation. There was something inside him which persuaded him she was worth exploring. He had convinced himself that a soul bent on criminality and deceit would not place themselves so honestly and publicly at the hands of a sex community. They would be more discrete, more adept at concealment. Every action would be carefully considered. In contrast, this lady was verifiably genuine and, as such, deserved the same respect and courtesy afforded to anyone else who cared to put themselves out in the market for forbidden pleasures.

The trafficking charge had been an interesting one in itself. It wasn't evidenced by the Hollywood sensationalised suitcases of money and clear plastic bags filled with fine white powder. It wasn't the result of an elaborate hydroponics cannabis farm hidden in a disused block of flats hadn't been discovered either. No, somehow the gang she had been associated to had sewn long tubes of heroin into a Persian rug and simply attempted to import the tapestry into the country.

When Tif had unearthed her criminal record, he had tried to gently sound her out through their exchanges, insisting on the importance of honesty and openness in these types of sexual relationships. He questioned her, 'I'm sure I have seen you somewhere.

You're positive we have never met?' But she wouldn't confirm anything. After a few exchanges, he had determined his gentle approach was insufficient to open the door containing her history. So he had resorted to a more direct approach. She had initially been shocked, almost angry that she had been exposed.

But when Tif failed to make a big thing out of it, a calmness had returned to her words. She seemed almost relieved, then subsequently intrigued to find out that the burgeoning relationship had survived. Tif had no way of ever knowing her true culpability in the endeavour. All he knew was that she was in her twenties at the time, and received the lightest incarceration sentence of them all. Later she had told him that she had simply been young, naïve and too trusting of those around her. A declaration Tif had accepted because it was issued with unreserved accountability for her actions and a statement of hard-fought redemption. As such, it had all the trappings of an admirable and genuine confession that deserved to be embraced as an epitaph to a regrettable chapter in her life.

Thus, they decided to meet. She arrived a few minutes late, with her six-month-old daughter cradled in the back of an SUV. Tif had always felt there was something intangible in parenthood that bestowed an innate faith in the goodness of an adult accountable for nurturing a young human. This belief was challenged every day by the news of parental abuse, but relying on probabilities, and seeing her in person, in this instance, on this occasion, he felt the shoe fit.

They sat in her car for less than an hour. He had bought her a cappuccino and a blueberry muffin. As they talked, they covered her conviction, their relationships, their desires and their wants from any meetings. She was polite, meek and a little nervous. All traits that seemed to reinforce the character profile he had formed. Her name was

Abda, which meant extraordinary in Arabic, original, beautiful. She was indeed all of those things. She was development number one and he was hooked like a salmon. In conclusion, they arranged to meet for a 'try out' the following week.

Development number two had equally been bizarre. Tif had come into personal contact through emails with an elderly gentleman who represented a couple searching on the same community website. He, Lochlyn, was Scottish, in his seventies, and had been married to his third wife, Natali, for eight years, and who was twenty-seven years his junior. As with her predecessors, she was from a former Soviet Union state, precisely from Ukraine, and spoke Russian as her native tongue. In her younger years, she had been a professional dancer for over twenty years. But according to Lochlyn, as is the law in Ukraine, she was forced to retire at the age of thirty-five. Living in a former Communist country continually trying to westernise through successive, fragile, multi-party coalition governments, the prospects for work beyond her vocation were few. So she had ended up waitressing in a local café in Donetsk, a small industrial city sitting on the banks of the Kalmius River in the south-eastern part of the country. It was here that she had met Lochlyn.

Tif hadn't met Natali yet, but he had seen some pictures, both of her as she was now and also from her professional heyday. She was short, around five foot four, and tastefully muscular, with athletes' breasts. Her thighs and calves looked powerful and he had imagined being nestled between them. Her auburn hair was shoulder length, with a straight fringe just above the eyebrow. She had porcelain white skin and an appealing face, but with a closed-lip smile that suggested apprehension. He did not want to segment the incredible majesty of nature, but she looked every bit Russian. So Russian that if he had been asked to draw a Russian woman, he may well have drawn Natali.

Lochlyn could only have been described as an old rogue. With two ex-wives and ex-Ukrainian dancer a third of his age at his side, how else could he be described? He was a very pleasant rogue though, but Tif was a little reticent about engaging with them. It wasn't that he found Natali unattractive, on the contrary he found her very agreeable. It was that Lochlyn had told him he had collapsed at work barely twelve months ago. Passed out stone cold. He had been diagnosed with a heart condition and had gone under the knife to have stents inserted in his arteries. Having received this experience as a wake-up call, Lochlyn had heeded the warning and gone for a comprehensive medical assessment. Whether he was considered fortunate or not, this health check unravelled the onset of prostate cancer. After test-work, the growth had been determined benign, so he had elected the 'do nothing' approach and retained the same lifestyle, while keeping a periodic check on the evolution of this condition.

Life had apparently continued as usual for him until about three months ago when, during the lead-up to Christmas, he had had a heart attack. In fact, not just one, but three in a single day. For which the medical recommendation was to insert a pacemaker. That operation had been completed expediently and Lochlyn had started the process of recovery. Given the previous health shocks, this event had been the last nail in the coffin of the couple's marital sex life. While they loved each other without question, Natali feared that any such stimulation would inevitably deliver dire consequences and refused to risk her final memories of Lochlyn be of him gasping for breath, wide-eyed, clutching at his chest, as her solid, perfectly-crafted thighs straddled his waist. Thus, in an effort to find a solution to express her needs other than through accessories, Lochlyn had proposed she took on a lover. And so their search had begun.

All had seemed very credible to Tif, yet his brain couldn't help but continually assess the risks of every detail of their story. Had she received her right to remain, therefore allowing her to live in the UK, or was he being lined up to enable that in some bizarre way? Or was it all an attempt to find a replacement for Lochlyn, should mortality take him sooner rather than later? Or could it be that this was some sort of female midlife crisis that drove the need to fill a looming void with a desire to have a baby, and with her husband's condition, usurping sperm from an unsuspecting donor was a more practical solution? All these things had given rise to caution, and yet he couldn't help himself from stumbling forward with the relationship and had begun making arrangements with Lochlyn for a first social meeting.

Fortunately, the third and fourth developments had been less awkward. The third development had been a couple from Redcar, a town next to Middlesbrough. He had seen pictures of the woman, body shots from various angles, some of which were not even flattering, but they were an interesting couple and open to ideas. The exchanges had been unstructured and sporadic. Consequently, Tif had struggled to build up much of a profile. He knew there was a nineteen-year age gap between them. They had two kids, who were eleven and four. He was working, she had recently been made redundant. They were happy to travel and meet in laybys, something Tif wasn't necessarily keen on doing, but their willingness did represent a clear statement of intent to find pleasure under any circumstances. The only other information he had deduced from their exchanges was that they were either British and highly illiterate—the latter being an unfortunate product of inhabiting within a community devastated by the decline of the industrial revolution—or they were foreign, with a limited grasp of the English language. He assumed this because their text messages were akin to those written by a teenager, where spelling is considered irrelevant and time-consuming, as long as the phonics make the correct sound. It was only because of their seemingly unguarded, liberated approach to meaningless and functional encounters that Tif had tolerated the absence of one of the 'three Rs'.

The fourth development had been a couple from Leeds, both the same age as Tif and in a cuckold relationship. Now, Tif was inexperienced in such things, but he had always been intrigued. He knew such a relationship meant the woman was generally the recipient of excessive submissive attention. But Tif was still unclear whether there was a convention as to who held the power base. Was it the man demanding his woman offer herself up for pleasure or the woman tormenting her spouse by making him witness her lust laid bare? It was really confusing, but as with the Redcar couple, this couple had been available with minimal effort. The lady, Sue, had bobbed blonde hair, a round face, and a smile that made her eyes sparkle. And with it, that rare ability to exude such a joyousness that couldn't be ignored, reflecting a happy contentment with everything in her world. She wasn't particularly tall, standing five foot four without high heels, which was probably why she favoured heels. Though petite in height, Sue was fuller-figured. Not obese, but she had perfectly filled every inch of the floral dress she wore when they had met at a coffee shop for a get-to-know-you.

Sue had met Tif with her husband, Gav, a rather large-framed black gentleman. Gav was an exceptionally engaging guy. Open, warm, genuine, down to earth. Tif could have continued to characterise him with positive references, but the long and short of it was that he felt comfortable around them. Gav was taller than his wife, probably scaling a couple of inches higher than Tif. He had large hands, which led Tif to reflect on the age-old anatomical association between hand span and genitalia. Which in turn led to him being concerned that his endowment may prove inadequate to provide the service they were seeking.

A cute convict. A widow in waiting. A social sex-fiend. And a curvaceous cuckold. From the outside, considering Tif's history and such opportunities, it was challenging to see what was the issue he faced, what left him drawing closer to the precipice. For a man who had savoured so much of what life had to offer, but done so with a modicum sense of respect and reasonable courtesy, why should this convergence of circumstance give rise to a dilemma of such magnitude? Two words swiftly explained that. Two words that cut through male pride and confidence. Words he dreaded. The fifth development. *Erectile dysfunction.*

The first time he had explained this in private to me, he had questioned whether, in the shadow of his self-evident physical impediment, developments one to four could hold alternative meaning. The convict representing a desire for danger, the Ukrainian a white night complex, the Redcar couple a sordid deviance, and the Leeds couple a desire for dominance. Viewed separately, each opportunity was unremarkable. However, when analysed as a collective, they could illustrate a sub-conscious, escalating, compensatory emotional stimulant. Like a shot of adrenaline to renew his manhood. At least that was what he believed.

IT'S ALL ABOUT TRIANGLES

"Everything is triangles tonight! What's that all about? Maslow. Karpman." Tif joked.

"Blame those two." Addi pointed at Newt and Hawkshaw.

"It's not my fault so much can be explained through three connected points!" Newt replied with a smile.

"It's all crap anyway." Tif retorted. "And I'm not certain it's helping anyone!"

He particularly meant it wasn't helping him and never had. Even if his journey of discovery had possibly been more disastrous than mine. At least he seemed as if he knew where he was mentally. Whereas I didn't. He had subconsciously began to project an acceptance that his addiction was a negative immoral act, executed to deliver a positive feeling. Something to raise him momentarily from his own feelings of utter emptiness. In stark contrast, I struggled to characterise anything in my own behaviour. It was probably because of my numbness that I was the only one who saw his acknowledgement of his state of mind.

"That's because you're an addict." Hawkshaw declared again on behalf of them all. "You don't want to see patterns. Don't want to acknowledge your behaviour is anything more than you exerting your free will. And you persist in failing to see the consequences of your actions."

"That's not true! Everyone I meet is a willing participant!" Tif argued.

Hawkshaw stared at him. "Are your family willing participants? Are they benefiting from all your antics?" Tif said nothing. "I don't think so. So maybe there is a triangle out there for you that you might relate to."

There was a triangle out there Tif would relate to, given his current condition. One that medicalised addiction. Put it in language that he had now begun to suffer the biological symptoms of. Erectile dysfunction.

"I can immediately think of a couple of models..." Newt announced cautiously, as if she feared our response. Or more specifically, Tif's jibes.

"Pray, do enlighten me." Tif delivered on her expectation and her face sunk.

"Ignore him." Hawkshaw encouraged. "He's bound not to like what you've got to offer, so say it anyway." Newt's face relaxed again.

"Well, the first model is designed to help understand what draws people like Tif and Ethan into reliance or dependency on something to find comfort." She paused, as if she was considering how to explain it best. "Imagine you've got your triangle. You've got the three points, or the vertices, connected by three lines, or sides. Unlike other models, rather than each vertices having a clear definition, with the connecting lines representing journeys or behavioural pathways to migrate from one specified state to another, the triangle has mass, with the three criteria filling the void and merging together like a jigsaw."

"Not sure I understand?" I objected.

"Okay, so other models have three points of behaviour and you can only travel between each. This model is a bit like a kid's drawing, it allows you to exist and travel anywhere inside the triangle. So imagine that there is a point at the centre of the triangle and we connect each vertices to that central point with a line. We'd then have three more triangles. Now colour those in separate colours and accept now that anywhere within the triangle you can exist on a journey."

"So there are numerous transient states you can exist at?" Hawkshaw sought clarity.

"Exactly! It offers a more fluid representation of addiction. Allowing primary, secondary and tertiary driving forces, all acting collectively at any point in time, because addiction isn't a static state."

"So what are the three elements of trauma embodied in this triangle?" Tif asked.

"Emotional, behavioural and physical." Newt replied succinctly.

"How does this triangle help Tif?" Addi asked.

"Well, as I've listened to his exploits, there has definitely been an increasing need for emotional connection. A need for the encounters to yield more than physical gratification." She addressed Tif directly. "It's like your addiction has developed an imperative for a personal connection over time. A connection that expands the period of elation from a moment's ejaculation."

"Harsh." Tif protested.

"It's nothing to feel ashamed about! It's quite a common progression for someone seeking extramarital stimulation! Such things begin with a belief that you crave sex, but steadily understand that it is meaningless in absence of emotional presence." She clarified.

"So if that's my emotional trauma, what's my behavioural?" Tif challenged.

"The fact that you can find the experiences relaxing because they are detached from your life. They offer you a chance to be someone you aren't usually allowed to be. Freedom from reality."

"I can't deny I've had some fantastical moments!" He smirked.

"Yes, but what you've persistently failed to acknowledge is how those endeavours have fed back into reality and modified the way you behave in your real life." She redressed.

"That's rubbish!" Tif objected.

"So you deny the habitual checking of Kik, WhatsApp, emails and websites for messages? Doesn't that activity consume a disproportionate part of your waking hours? Doesn't it affect your productivity?" Tif had no defence to offer, so she went on. "And because you dedicate so much time to lewd correspondence, you compress all the things you need to accomplish for work and home, into an ever-decreasing period of time. This has given you stress and anxiety, which swells from the deceit, and manifests every now and then in bursts of intolerance and anger. Such explosions driving your need for further detachment and rewarding relaxation. It's a viciously damaging downward spiral that I wish you could accept."

Like a dog with a bludgeoned nose, Tif cowered back, looking almost embarrassed in his seat.

"What about the physical?" Addi prompted.

"That's simply a function of gender." She smirked. "As they say, a man thinks about sex every seven seconds and a woman significantly less."

"I don't know if that is a credible statistic." Hawkshaw uncharacteristically questioned Newt.

"But you can't refute that, in general, women need a reason, men only need a place?" She replied smugly. "Besides, whatever the driving force, whether it's the arousal, the plateau or the orgasm stage of sex, it offers a euphoria unequalled in the natural world, and it is something that Tif has very much savoured and finds difficult to walk away from."

"Sounds like Newt has a triangle for you after all!" Hawkshaw declared.

"Wait, there's more!" She announced.

"Not sure I can take any more!" Tif replied, somewhat dejected.

"What that model fails to explicitly account for is whether addiction is a moral deviance or a medical illness. Over time, humanity has significantly altered its views on this. Successive generations evolving to offer an increasing tolerance of deviance in society, such that today, actors like Tif are not considered deviants as such. They remain a minority. And one that acts at odds with the dominant accepted social norms. But they are almost passively accepted."

"I'm not sure society accepts adulterers." Hawkshaw cautioned.

"I disagree! We may not like it, but we accept it. It's why divorces began in the first place. It's why the youth of today have several relationship classifications before labelling themselves boyfriend and girlfriend, so that commitment is deferred."

Hawkshaw remained silent.

"Tolerance aside," she continued, "it has been this point of contrast between the morality of dominant and minority players that has forced a further change in society. The minority has become so prevalent that we can't just turn a blind eye anymore. We have had to find solution to the increasing sexual liberalisation that civilisation is expected to accept. It has to be explained. There has to be a reason. And for that, many doctors, professors, and researchers have laboured to medicalise the addiction."

"I don't believe in that." Hawkshaw affirmed.

"You don't have to, not everyone does. Unfortunately, the masses rule and the masses need a reason to accept!" She paused for comment, but none was forthcoming, so she carried on. "One model for medicalisation, based on a triangle," she smiled, "considers addiction as a disease, spread by three factors: genetics, neurochemical and social environment. Genetics apportions the blame at the feet of hereditary biology. Neurochemical imbalance favours a more scientific association between testosterone and a need for gratification. While social environment approaches infer that immersion in an immoral culture can ultimately overcome anybody's restraint and lead them to deviate. Effectively 'societal nurture'. To me, all diagnoses are plausible."

The table fell silent. I took a moment to look around the room and witnessed once more the barman staring over, his face strained with puzzlement.

"Tif, was your dad like you?" Newt inquired.

"What do you mean?"

"Did he have an affair?" She clarified.

"Hell no! He was as monogamous as can be!" Tif was clearly offended.

"Have you ever been tested for testosterone levels?" She switched tack.

"No. Not something I've ever had a problem with. Which I thought would be self-evident!" But he sounded less self-assured. "Actually...that's a lie. I did a blood test recently, and it showed that my testosterone levels were just above the minimum 'normal' range. Not really surprising...with my life, I've probably used up more than my fair share."

Then he attempted to make light of the revelation. I saw Addi smile and assumed he was wondering what it must have been like. So much sex that natural hormones were depleted. I was certain everyone in our group assumed Addi never had thoughts like that. Assumed his high morals and family adoration was infused in his soul, making the attainment of purity effortless. We had him on a pedestal of righteousness. It was unjust. He also had temptations.

Recently, in the face of Tif's debauchery, he had gotten closer to needing to see what such loss of inhibitions and scruples would feel like. But rather than succumb, he had focused on managing such considerations through simple acts, also known as coping mechanisms, that addicts use to overcome their cravings. First, delaying acting on the impulse, finding ways to let time serve to reduce his desire, forcing willpower to provide the strength to wait. Secondly, breathing deeply to stabilise his heart rate. Focusing on calmer and more rational thoughts. Thirdly, focusing on distraction from the obsessive thoughts. Finally, water. Drinking water was an odd one, really. Addi couldn't explain why it worked but it did. Whether it was a distraction, a method to delay, a foundation for calming his breathing, or just a means to fill his bladder and deliver penial discomfort that frustrated erections. It didn't matter. Whichever approach he took, all had worked so far to

help maintain his integrity and protect the sanctity of his marriage and
family.

PATERNAL GUIDANCE

For Addi, the world revolved around his family. There was no endeavour too big to make his daughters' childhoods the best they could be. But they were getting older and his time for that was drawing to a close. His eldest was already reaching adulthood and, with it, he had been compelled to acknowledge two things. First, his idea of fun was becoming ever less hers. In other words, he should be nowhere to be seen for her to really have fun. Secondly, he and his wife's influence over her was diminishing. This wasn't a revelation. In fact, he had long been reconciled with letting go, always professing that the primary objective of parenting was to hope he would find a lifelong friend. That aspiration being continually challenged by the stereotype of parents' thrust on their kids by their ever-evolving and fluctuating peer groups.

The result of these conflicting influences was that parenting never completely found a comfortable rhythm. It was never a static work of art, but a spontaneous and reactive evolution. The tools and techniques of which had to evolve continually to outwit the child. Command and control transformed into influence and containment, which then morphed into objective guidance, and eventually just hope. Hope that the education bestowed had been understood and embraced. And embedded within those eighteen years of imparted wisdom, the seeds of three consistent messages that repeated through every stage of development had taken root. To be with people who accepted the freedom to hold an opinion. To have respect to listen to the opinions of others without judgment. And to maintain the conviction to hold true to the values which form good opinion. Opinions above all else are the vehicle to independence. Knowing when to hold fast to your own or when to embrace someone else's is the key to growth. However, he had also confessed to me that, despite all his rationalising and preparation for relinquishing the parental reins, he had been unable to vocalise one final bout of wisdom when his eldest daughter had left for university. Just like when he had left his dad, tears had overcome him. Therefore, just like he had done for his father, he had written her a letter, on behalf of him and his wife.

Lydie,

There is never enough time in life to say the things we want to say or always the right time to say them. Now that you have turned eighteen, your mum and I have decided we would write you a letter, that you may always keep with you. Many of the sentiments expressed you have heard before and we hope you take them to heart, because we will always love you without measure.

Very early in your life we, your parents agreed on one thing: that our aim was to ensure you would be someone you could be proud of and that you would be our friend for life.

Being your parents through your childhood has been a privilege. That doesn't mean it has been easy, but nothing in life worth doing is. Even through challenging times we have always had faith that you would grow into the woman you are today. Your confidence is admirable, your joy infectious, your temper terrifying, your emotional fragility concerning, your hugs warming, your intelligence pride filling, your compassion volatile, your beauty inside and out complete, your determination commendable and your friendship cherished. And with this declaration of friendship we offer some highlights of wisdom. Not quite the Ten Commandments, but tips that if someone had told us twenty-nine years ago we might have made some different decisions. So our tips for life. While you may want to belittle some of them, they are based on the experiences of two individuals who have seen a lot in their time and who offer their observations in absence of any selfish intent—just a desire to aid you in your journey as much as they can.

Live life without regret. That doesn't mean be ignorant of your actions and how they hurt or harm others around you, but be cognisant of your influence and endeavour to make the right decision, not just the easy decision, no matter how difficult that might be. We don't mean try not to make mistakes. That would be impossible. Mistakes are a form of education. You aren't giving it your all if you don't make some. Just try and see the pitfalls beforehand, so consequences can be measured and managed within the constraints of your own conscience.

Keep your family close at heart. Treat them as your best friends. It may be hard to see through proximity and the red mist of anger, but consider this: it is only with family that the full deception of life is stripped away and honest rhetoric exists. Blood really is thicker than water. No matter how dysfunctional relationships may at times seem to be with our siblings and parents, know that in your darkest times they have and will always be there to help you.

Don't try and plan everything in life. It is right to be ambitious and have short- or medium-term goals, but know that life will throw you curveballs you can't control. Plans will change and adapt, and if you believe in yourself, you will find a way forward. Approaching unexpected events as opportunities, and with positivity, will reduce your disappointment. Thereby increasing a sense of contentment which will lead to a happier existence.

217

Your integrity, ethics and morals define the person you are. You have probably heard us say before that we give trust to people when we meet them, and they lose it only once, because we lack the tolerance for lies. It is this characteristic that has contributed to change in our lives numerous times. For you and your sisters, it will be even more challenging, because we fear you will have to brave a world with diminishing regard for humanity, ethics and morals. Don't succumb to this declining code of social conduct. Be accountable for what you do. Take responsibility for your actions and know that by doing so, your value system is enriched.

Be brave. That doesn't mean base-jump off buildings. That's crazy. But don't be afraid to try new things and push your nerves. Push them while taking a sensible view of your capabilities and push them with an eye on rationality, risks and consequences.

Respect your body. You only get one body and one opportunity to look after it or treat it with disregard. If we could tell our younger selves four things it would be: 'Well done for not smoking. Well done for not taking drugs. Well done for keeping relatively fit. But for heavens-sake, cut down on the alcohol!'. There will most likely be a time in life when you go to the doctors and have to accept that some part of your physiology is in decline, so try to live to delay that date and ensure that whatever it is, it is declining through natural wear and tear alone. Remember, live life well and with love. With love you can be on a perpetual high without any form of stimulant.

Accept age as a part of life. There is no point ever lamenting over bat wings, sagging boobs, crow's feet or hair loss (heaven forbid!). The linear nature of life hits us all. How you look is never what defines you. Acknowledge it. Embrace it. Make the most out of it. Know society will likely never see more beauty in you than during the years before you

218

turn thirty and dismiss it as a ridiculous judgement. External beauty is not what defines us. How we look is superficial when it comes to love. So know that you will always be beautiful to those that care for you and take that care to accept and embrace every element of who you are.

See the world and embrace cultural differences. Connectivity and air travel have made the world more accessible. Use them to see and experience what you want. You know we have always sorted to show you as much as we can, and have ranked our travels in higher regard than any possession. Our time and shared experiences with you and your sisters have always brought us joy, as well as given us purpose in our lives. The saying is true, 'Work to live. Don't live to work'.

Sing! Music is a soundtrack to life. A point of association for adventures and key moments in your journey. And above all else, it is just simply good for the soul to let yourself be heard above the din of society.

Love. We believe we have given you a good grounding on the importance of love. Love for your family. Love for yourself and for finding true love in another. In a lifetime companion. Don't believe in the Hollywood fairytale though! Finding true love in another is never a gentle path. No two people are the same; it is usually the differences that stimulate the initial attraction. Don't give your love freely, but be open to seeing when you think someone in your life deserves your unconditional love. Know that in giving it, you will have to tread the tight rope between compromise and holding true to your values. The art to a successful and loving partnership is when these aspirations are continuously met by both parties with equal desire to find a way forward, not to find an excuse for an end.

Know that luck is a gift and an architect of life. It is part luck that you were born to us. It is part luck that you were born in one of a few nations that are considered developed. It is part luck that you have had the childhood you have had. Your experience of this world is not what the majority experience. Many are less fortunate. Don't take that foundation for granted. Use that gift to make something of yourself so you can give back to the world and help others grow. So that you can find yourself in a position to be able to make other people's lives a little better. Pay it forward.

Be more kind. Yes, I know we are ripping that off Frank, but what the hell! It's a meaningful statement of intent. It doesn't mean you will be a doormat for anyone. It is just a declaration not to act with malice and to know that even the smallest things can make another person's day, morning, hour or minute better. No matter what you know about your life, you never truly understand what others are going through.

This letter is not an epitaph of parenthood. We will be your parents for as long as we breathe. We are here to listen. To talk, without judgement. To offer advice, without obligation. To provide sanctuary and protection, should you ever need it. To defend you, should you ever need it. To help you in any way that it is in our capability to do so. The world is big, it is challenging, and it is filled with many who will not deserve or appreciate what you have to offer professionally or personally. But know this: while we walk the Earth with you, you will never be alone. We are proud to be your parents, but now it is time for you to step forward on your own and be proud of yourself.

With all our love for always,

Mum and Dad

Addi told me his daughter had read the letter but had offered no comment. As much as he wanted to hear her thoughts, her vocal reaction, he treated that moment as the tipping point. The point where the balance of accountability for their relationship had shifted in her favour. It was an acceptance that she had to grow and decide what their relationship would become. So if she didn't want to say anything, that was okay.

Two years from that day, he said he had felt rewarded. The path she had chosen was everything he had hoped for. She was a friend. Now he hoped the same would be true for her sisters when their time came.

Posture, Language and Mental Focus

I looked over at Newt. She looked exhausted by the evening and was retreating back into herself. All of a sudden, like she had concluded she had contributed as much as she felt she could tonight, she stood up to leave. Making her excuses, she squeezed around the booth and gave me a kiss on the cheek and departed. Her exit was met with quiet reflection as the rest of us rebalanced ourselves to the shrinking representation.

"Good riddance there!" Tif exclaimed.

"Don't be so daft!" Hawkshaw replied.

"It's 'model this, model that'!" Tif ignored him.

"She's just explaining what has worked for her!" Addi stated.

"And there's a lot of sense in it!" Hawkshaw supported. "But I guess she does need to recognise that models aren't the antidote for everything."

"None of it jives with me!" Tif remarked.

"That's because you're in denial, mate!" Hawkshaw proposed. "And I think you know it."

Like me, I felt everyone else had slowly started to see through Tif tonight. Newt had elevated his addiction from the shadows. Now Hawkshaw was accusing him of being dishonest in his voluntarily blinkered behaviour.

"Depression or addiction, it's a choice! That's where I disagree with Newt!" Hawkshaw declared resolutely. "We spend all this time trying to understand why people behave the way they do and overlook the simplest fact, that behaviour *is* a choice. Doesn't matter how much we want to explain it away. When it comes down to it, individuals make conscious choices of action and inaction. Depression and addiction are just ways our bodies choose to manage how we feel about those choices!" His words were black and white. Unequivocal.

"Agreed." Addi offered his endorsement.

"What, so other people can't influence how you feel?" Tif questioned the simplicity of Hawkshaw's binary explanation.

"Not necessarily. Other people may influence how your decisions turn out. They offer forks in the road that may not be what you wanted or expected, but that's all they are. Just forks in the road. Turning points. It's still an individual's choice to decide how to act in that moment." He spoke very matter of fact.

"What about bullying? Harassment?" Tif queried.

"You know my views on that! There are prosholes everywhere in the world. No one can change that. All we can affect is how we react to their impact on us." Hawkshaw replied. "I'm not avoiding prosholes, but I am not suffering them either. You don't see me letting them get into my head and deconstruct my confidence, self-esteem or ambition. Because that's a choice!"

Tif knew Hawkshaw's words were hard to contradict. But as was evident in the world, and with me, not everybody was blessed with the same level of zeal and resilience to keep marching on in ignorance of the hits thrown their way.

"Act positive. Be positive. Don't wallow." Hawkshaw declared. "That's my view."

"Some days that's easier than others." I replied with subdued contestation. In one sentence, I announced that the needle of depression hadn't moved far following the night's consultation.

"Back to square one then!" Tif remarked. "Where's Newt when you need her!?"

"Ethan, I'm not suggesting you click you fingers and suddenly everything will be okay. I've seen people do that and it's just a mask to disguise what lays underneath. It doesn't help anyone." Hawkshaw addressed me directly. "I accept we all have different thresholds and rates of change, but recovery is about taking positive steps forward. Sometimes it's the small things that provide the greatest benefits."

From across the room, the barman looked over once more, puzzled by the activity from our table. I allowed myself to stare at him a little longer, likewise bemused by his interest in our table. He was an older man, probably in his mid-fifties. His face haggard from the hands-on long hours of being a pub landlord. Thin hair, protruding belly that strained his shirt buttons and weathered hands, he exhibited all the signs of a man confined to menial indoor labour. And typical of people in his spatially-constricted profession, his inquisitive nature had become overactive. Hawkshaw had also noticed the extra attention, but had evidently thought nothing of it. If the man wanted to listen in, then Hawkshaw had concluded it was immaterial. We weren't doing anything unusual or illegal.

"It's about three things." Hawkshaw continued.

"Bloody three things again!" Tif objected, incredulous.

Hawkshaw ignored him. "Posture. Language. Mental focus." He paused to let the words sink in and for Tif to make a comment. "There's a link between how people hold themselves and their moods. You see someone with slumped shoulders and arched back, what do you think?"

"Having a bad day?" Addi proposed.

"Exactly!" Hawkshaw continued. "If you see someone standing tall, with their shoulders pushed back, you see confidence. Well, your body sees exactly the same in you. Your nerves characterise your posture and inform your brain how to feel." He didn't wait for further comment before pressing on. "The language we use is also a marker for assessing moods. Words can be positive, negative or ambivalent. People will use those markers to understand and engage with you. If you wake up every day and declare you're depressed, then you'll feel depressed." Hawkshaw was again blunt to the verge of brutality. "You have to find a way to use positive words to describe things. Start small. I'm not suggesting you flick a switch, but just open your eyes enough to see the positives in your life and, like an actor, use those to inform your choice of words."

"Look positive, speak positive?"

Hawkshaw ignored Tif's cynicism once more. "Finally, it's about mental focus. It can be tough when you're out of work. Society has built this construct that having a job is a necessity, that being out of work is embarrassing and means you're inadequate; that it is a job that gives you purpose. Bollocks! Look at Addi! Love and family are all he needs to give him purpose. And I think he's right. That is the foundation. Newt was also right. There are basic needs in life that make us feel whole! I don't know if Maslow can lay claim to knowing what they are for everyone, but he was on the right track."

Addi seemed uncomfortable at the idea of being used as a reference for understanding the meaning of life, because he had entrusted me once with the truth that even he had skirmished with temptation. In reality, Newt had been very close to the facts when she'd expressed concern over Tif's influence on him.

"You have so much good in your life." Hawkshaw resumed his counsel. "You have a wonderful wife and incredible kids. I know you see that, but you need to be open to being happy about that. Yes, you don't have a job at the moment, but look at all you have accomplished in life! Do you honestly believe this is the end of your story?" He paused, waiting for a reply. I didn't oblige. "My recommendation to you is to focus on giving structure to your days. Fill them with things that you can achieve and build a sense of accomplishment."

"Such as?" Tif probed.

"Exercise. Maybe not every day, but every other day. Read. Keep your brain active. Be in the world. Go sit in a coffee shop for an afternoon, talk with the baristas. Be present in the world. Develop yourself. Learn a skill or get another professional accreditation. I mean, you've got so many letters after your name it's ridiculous, but nothing to prevent you adding to them. All of these things may seem simple, but sometimes it's the simplest things that offer the greatest sense of worth. All of that positivity can then fuel your search for your next challenge. Don't see it as a job. It's a challenge you want. Not a 9-to-5!"

"Have you ever considered becoming a motivational speaker?" Tif joked. Hawkshaw dismissed him again. Unlike Newt, he refused to be drawn into distraction by their wayward friend.

"And I would advise you to stop drinking! Or at least take the step to cut it out for five days a week and cap yourself to no more than three drinks on the nights you do." His tone dropped. "I accept people find comfort in the detachment that drink provides. But it's temporary. The reality is that with the comfort comes relaxation and that opens the floodgates for your thoughts to wonder. Trust me, you'll take more steps backward than forward with every sip. It's not an answer, but not drinking across those five days would be another accomplishment you can acknowledge and build on."

Hawkshaw looked at each of us in turn, seeking acceptance or at least some acknowledgement of his beliefs. I knew he could see from our expressions that he had struck a chord with Tif and I. He could tell we were reflecting on the impact of our current lifestyle choices, our addictions. Addi on the other hand, seemed surprisingly uncomfortable.

"Look, there's nothing more I can add." He slid out of the booth and stood up. "You either recognise it and decide to try or you don't. In the end, the decision can only be yours."

With these last words, he extended his hand towards me in parting. I reached back respectfully and we shook.

"Whatever you decide, you take care of yourself."

The suddenness of Hawkshaw's departure left a larger vacuum than when Newt left. I knew Tif was struggling with that as much as I was. His face was visibly consumed by what I could only guess were uncomfortable thoughts. As the night had progressed, the conversation had thrown more and more at his feet, increasingly unravelling his belief system. Whilst it may be a somewhat perverse belief system, it was an anchor that he felt kept him sane. An anchor without which he may well follow me down into the pit of despair.

AN EPIPHANY

"I can say this now that Newt's gone." Tif took a deep breath and we all waited for him to continue. "I initially self-diagnosed my diminishing carnal desires to be the result of apathy spawned from a life of excess, precipitating in erectile dysfunction. I had been wrong. It wasn't an excess of flirtatious interludes that had driven me to mental indifference and penial insurrection. It was a sub-conscious emergence that while I engaged to understand my partners more, create a social connection, true affection always remained absent."

"Did Newt help you come to that conclusion?" I asked.

"No. Although she's right in all she says. But don't tell her I said that, she'd become even more insufferable in her self-righteousness." He grinned.

"She's not like that. She just wants what's best for each of us. That's love!" Addi offered.

"If it is not her who led you to your epiphany, who or what is it?" I probed.

For a second, Tif looked as if he were going to retrench and say nothing, but something inside him evidently urged him on. "It started when I met a lady called Lisa on one of my websites. She was twenty-eight years old, short, slim, with deep purple hair and a pretty face. She also happened to live just seven miles away from me. Which was hugely convenient. I had sent her a simple message, a really innocuous greeting, for which I had held little expectation of an answer. I was surprised when one arrived within minutes. Her message was direct. Somewhat harsh. In each subsequent exchange I felt like there was a veiled contempt. I was a bit flummoxed about whether to carry on talking with the perceived embedded passive aggressive attitude in her words. But there was also this kind of detached genuineness to her messages that I found really interesting."

"You've always favoured quirky chicks!" Addi offered.

Tif agreed. "Anyway, I was the second person she had talked with. She'd chatted to another guy, taking it all the way to agreeing to meet for a coffee. But she couldn't go through with it. Said when she had arrived outside the coffee shop, she'd had a sudden rush of anxiety, a foreboding causing her to walk away. And once she'd explained more about herself to me, the apprehension was completely understandable."

"What do you mean?"

"Her life had been troubled in many ways. She'd fallen pregnant at the age of seventeen, and while she said she was incapable now of explaining, had allowed the father, her then boyfriend, to convince her to keep their baby. But after twenty-five weeks, one week beyond the date she could have received an abortion, he had taken flight. Leaving her to fend for herself."

"Absolute coward!" Addi declared vehemently.

"Her parents had disowned her as well, so she was all on her own."

"That sucks! I could never disown my kids!" Addi announced, unnecessarily as we all knew that.

"She had a son and soon afterwards met a new guy. She said he seemed alright and their relationship grew, but never to the point where she allowed him to move into her home. Which in the end proved to be a good decision because, as time passed, the relationship became distressed, and by that I mean the guy threatened her. Not her directly, but her son."

"Why?" Addi asked.

"She never said. She just told me she had continually offered herself up for sacrifice. Then one day, her submission had been insufficient and he had punched her. It was the start of the end, but not the rational end of two humans agreeing they desired different things from life. It was more twisted than that." He paused briefly. "Unknown to Lisa, he had made himself a copy of her house keys and late one night, allegedly possessed by evil thoughts, he entered her house. She had woken just in time to stop him hurting her son, but nearly paid the ultimate price. He stabbed her four times, then shot her in the leg. Her bravery nearly deprived her son of his mother that night."

"Jesus!" Addi didn't know what else to say.

"She was declared clinically dead for sixty seconds. But she'd refused to die and fought her way back into the world. Such was her determination to be there for her kid."

"I know people say things like that, but do you really think the motivations of the soul can really bring you back to life?" I asked.

"I don't know, but she did come back from the dead. How she chooses to glamorise it is up to her. I was just in awe of her selflessness."

"Rightly so..." Addi agreed.

"Anyway, it obviously took her a while after that to trust anyone again. But she did. Trusted a man for whom she would later tattoo his name on her back. A man she decided to have a second child with. Another son. A man who offered her marriage, which she accepted. A man who then left her the week before their wedding to move in with another woman. A man who she then discovered had accrued ten thousand pounds worth of debt, which she was obligated to repay. A despicable man. A man absent of remorse for his callousness."

"Not being funny, but did you believe all this?" Addi queried. "I mean, there's bad luck and there's appalling luck!"

"Yes, I believed her. The way she spoke about her past. There's no way that emotion could be faked. And why? She gained nothing by lying about it."

"I guess so." Addi conceded.

"So far she'd had three men in her life, each wielding the worst of humankind's behaviour, wilfully setting out to breach the seventh, eighth and ninth Commandments. *Thou shall not commit murder, nor commit adultery, nor steal.*"

"I've never taken you for the religious type?" Addi quipped.

"Five years of Sunday school and studying Divinity at school until I was fourteen. Some of it had to sink in!"

"That kind of trauma while so young must have anesthetised her a bit to life?" I commented.

"That's what I thought too. It gave me fresh consideration as to the source of her bluntness!"

"So what happened?" Addi asked.

"She had been largely uninquisitive with me, approaching the conversation very transactional in nature. She was just seeking an uncomplicated way to satisfy an emotionally detached need. She wanted to be used, not degraded. Wanted to relinquish control for short interludes where every decision would be made by her chosen accomplice. Craved to feel out of control, but safe. She had this fantasy of being unable to prevent being taken. I'd been a little consumed by the *déjà vu* of Lucinda, and wrestled with trying to understand why a woman who had endured so much suffering by the hands of those who sorted to eradicate her control on life would recreationally wish to relinquish title to her body. In the end though, I had reconciled such inquiry as her decision to make and agreed to meet her for a coffee."

He sighed and then continued. "We met at Starbucks. I was instantly charmed. We talked for two hours. It felt comfortable, almost familiar. I was obviously my usual affable, disarming self, and she sounded at ease, despite signs of the contrary, like her shaking hands and her refusal to make eye contact. On the infrequent occasions she looked directly at me, I remember this surprise in her eyes and an infectious smile blooming on her face. She had a great smile."

"Ah, the perv has feelings after all!" I joked.

"We started seeing each other after that. It was like an exclusive social relationship that included restrained physical stimulation. It wasn't dispassionate and we both knew that. There was a genuine affection between us which, in absence of the twenty-year age gap, might have flourished into something bigger. In fact, I was astonished at how the affection had persisted and grown. And the intimacy as a result was serene and my physical dysfunction absent. That was when I realised the true cause of my symptoms. It wasn't a side effect of nymphomania, but a need for heartfelt mental connection that had precipitated my impediment." Tif fell silent.

"What happened?" Addi prompted.

"I had an epiphany that brought equal joy and dilemma. I was joyous because the consumption of prescription drugs thirty minutes before standing to arms was reversible. I was still whole. Still complete. A fully functioning man. But I had begun to emotionally embrace a fact that I had buried. A truth that made me sick in the pit of my stomach. An acceptance that love and sex should not be mutually exclusive, or disjoint, but must be engaged in as co-dependent acts. And the reason I felt so sick was I had been pursuing the physicality away from a home in which I received and felt so much love."

FINDING CLARITY

In many ways, the withdrawal of Newt and Hawkshaw had left the greatest hole and instability. Both of them brought positive structure, strength and guidance. Now all that remained was my instability, Tif's deplorable excess and Addi's insular devotion. Not ingredients for the best therapy group.

"Has tonight helped at all?" Addi addressed me.

"I don't know..." I sat upright in my seat. "There's common sense mixed with noise. It's tough to pick through and immediately find an answer, I suppose."

"Do you feel like you're able to take a step forward then?" Tif questioned.

"Yes, I guess." I spoke with caution. "I know your path isn't one I want to try. It's tempting, yes, I've had opportunities without going on websites, but I don't see how it would help anything. It's just another layer of complication, surrounded by a plethora of emotions that I know I can't handle."

"I think that's a wise decision." Addi spoke with assured confidence, as if he empathised with the sentiment.

"Fair enough." Tif sounded slightly snubbed, despite having reached the same conclusion. "But it's your loss!"

And, with that, he stood up and readied himself to depart. "It's been a blast, but I'm out of here. Ethan, take care. Addi, keep loving."

"Thanks for coming, Tif!" I looked up at him.

"Always here if and when you decide you need me." Tif replied. "See you guys!"

He turned and walked across the bar, out the door. I watched him walk away. As if there was an idea within Tif's advocacy that I wasn't quite ready to forfeit and would evaporate if I lost sight of him. And as soon as the pub door slammed shut, the idea was gone.

"Our numbers are dwindling." Addi declared with a smile.

"Yes, but that's a good thing." I replied. "It brings clarity."

The landlord stared over once more. What he found so fascinating I didn't know, so I just smiled back. The rotund chap looked uncomfortable with the gesture and retreated to the other end of the bar. It was an awkward manoeuvre that left me regretting my pleasantness.

"I can see the sense in Newt's structures." I resumed talking. "There's nothing wrong in what she believes. I just fear believing in rigid models or doctrine too much would leave me exposed to failure, you know." I looked at Addi, who just stared back. "If it's too prescriptive and I keep falling short, all I'll do is reinforce my sense of worthlessness and negativity. But her points about health, security and love are really valid." I sighed.

Addi remained silent. I hadn't talked this much for a while tonight. Maybe he sensed that I was in the midst of some sort of a reconciliation. A soliloquy of solution discovery. My own epiphany.

"Hawkshaw made several valid points too. I agree with the majority of them. My good days are when I feel a sense of achievement and it is usually only small things." Raising my hands up to my cheeks, I swept them back soothingly over my head. "I agree with him on the posture and language piece also. It is a difficult one to maintain though. I've definitely found it especially challenging on days filled with bad news. Continually rolling with the punches is exhausting!" Sitting back in my seat, I gazed up at the ceiling.

My thoughts progressed privately. And with the silence I was sure Addi was beginning to feel increasingly redundant.

"Then there's you!" I grinned while shaking my head in disbelief. "So in love! One of the best humans I've ever known! Definitely one I like everything about!" My smile widened. "Your devotion for your family and your willingness to accept whatever life throws at you as long as your family is happy and healthy. In Newt's world, you have those bottom rungs of the ladder nailed and have transcended the remaining ones to find serenity."

"Don't be fooled! Reaching contentment hasn't been without challenges..." Addi contributed. "We all have obstacles to overcome and we all slip some time or other, falling short of perfection in pursuit of what we know to be important."

I could see traces of guilt across Addis' face but chose not to prompt him publicly for explanation.

"You are who you aspire to be, first and foremost." I declared.

The praise appeared to sit uncomfortably with Addi. He had recently told me of the things he had nearly done. The acts that had made receipt of Hawkshaw's praise feel disingenuous. Freedoms unavailable to him that he had almost entertained. I assumed that it was probably these events that now weighed him down with feelings of guilt and inadequacy.

HUMAN WEAKNESS

I've said before that Addi was full of love. Love and devotion for his family. But his pursuit towards father and husband of the year had been challenged once.

Tell me news. Three innocuous words, in isolation of any other fact. But when they'd arrived unexpectedly from someone Addi had never dared imagine might send them, they had taken on a life of their own.

The person in question was a former work colleague of his. A much younger lady who Addi openly admired and respected for her strength, determination and the potential she frequently neglected to see in herself. She was unimaginably captivating and, in her presence, it had taken every ounce of his will to remain focused on work.

It is often cited in life that everyone has a soulmate, it is simply a matter of finding them. The only variant to this statement Addi would make was to pluralise it. As an engineer, and having a firm foundation in mathematics, specifically probability, Addi found it implausible to conceive that, in a world of over six billion people, there was only one individual around whom he might find himself lost for words. But he did believe it was incredibly rare. In his life, he had only met two. One at the age of eighteen and one at the age of forty-four.

For the latter, his work colleague, it would be fair to say that, when he was first introduced to her, the potency of muteness had been significant. It may have been the age gap or self-deprecation on his behalf, but never in his wildest imaginings had Addi expected any reciprocation.

She was eighteen years his junior, lived in Rio de Janeiro, and was Brazilian. With a diminutive figure, she carried curves that within society's objectifying stereotype personified her nationality. Although short on stature, her personality was enormous. A personality that was larger than any he had ever known, with the sole exception of his father, and possibly John Lennon and Winston Churchill, though he had never met the last two on a personal level. She had brutally penetrating eyes that saw through any deceit, and which transformed into the most wondrous pools of beauty when she smiled. And what a smile she had! Blindingly large and bright! But she didn't reveal this softer side to everyone. There was never any deception or façade to her feelings. Her emotions were etched all over her body. To the un-indoctrinated she could seem cold, even callous in her judgement. Consequently, when she smiled, Addi came to appreciate its deep genuineness and because of that, he could almost feel the joy radiate from her. When he finally realised the smile was because of him, it had been impossible to preconceive the humbling effect it carried.

He had met her at an evening event for the company they worked for. He was part of the international team that oversaw operations in South America and she was an engineer. When he had entered the room that night, he had immediately noticed her. Though he couldn't recall what she had been wearing, he remembered his eyes were mesmerised by her beauty. As he had negotiated the room, talking to members of the regional team, one eye had been on his conversation partner while the other had remained fixed on her.

It would have been disingenuous to say at this point he was thinking about her as a soulmate. He was not that fickle. He had always professed it was beauty that established attraction, personality that shaped interest, character that created respect; and that it was only from the strength of passion forged as a product of these three attributes, that common garden love could be elevated to the ethereal status of soulmate. That evening, only attraction had been established. But an attraction so visceral that his gut ached.

Three years had passed in a blink of an eye since that moment. Addi had left the company twelve months before when the three-word message arrived. His first emotion had failed to match the beauty of the memories, being laced instead with suspicion. Living in a time fronted by fake news and catfishing, he was incapable of accepting the message as genuine. She had never given any indication of desiring a relationship beyond professional. As a consequence, he had interrogated the emailer to quell his fear. Exchange followed exchange, and with it his cynicism transformed to disbelief, then to happiness, then to rapture.

Several platonic events followed that first flurry of emails. Moments of serene serendipity that were held precious by him and would never be divulged because such moments were rare and deeply personal. Addi appreciated that in the current age of aspirational celebrity, driven by social media and reality television, purporting the merits of privacy was rapidly becoming considered a character flaw. But he would say to call him archaic; call him secretive; call him old-fashioned; he didn't care. While others castigated, he professed the strength of character required to hold something close to his heart and personal, would always far exceed the weakness to succumb to gossip or self-publicity and divulge to all. The relationship that had evolved inevitably ended. Not by his hand, but appropriately by her morals. It was an incontestable acknowledgement that the relationship was wrong. Platonic or not, such affection dangerously courted infidelity.

Sitting there tonight, much time had passed since the moment they had parted ways, all of it punctuated by messages between distant best friends who played with words to avoid saying the underlying truth that preserved the connection. For a moment, the messaging had been replaced by a brief meeting across a coffee table. At that time, eighteen months had passed since they had last spoken and maybe both of them had hoped the passage of time would have afforded emotional release. And for Addi, while the absence had allowed him to find his senses again, he remained enraptured.

So much in that brief meeting was left unsaid. Words which he hoped one day she may hear and understand. He had longed to tell her that they had had something so beautiful. Shared a time so pure and perfect that it could never be ignored. But the brilliance of that period had been hidden from the world. It remained their secret. A dream protected from reality. For days since the coffee meeting, he had wanted to write her a letter. The most honest letter she might ever receive. Not a letter that compelled her to answer immediately, if ever. An absence of response could never make theirs an unrequited affection, just an unattainable one. He simply wanted her to know, for him, it was an unattainable affection that would linger until his last breath. The memories of that cherished interlude bringing immeasurable and continuous warmth to his soul.

It is often said that risks must be taken if people are to become the best version of themselves and love is the greatest risk of all. Addi recalled someone had once said, 'Love is from another realm. We cannot manufacture it on demand. Nor can we subdue it when it appears. Love is not our choice to make.' But it is solely our choice to accept.

All these things he desired to tell her, but didn't. This time, he chose for them both. Deciding that such verse would only make her heart hurt. He knew her decision had been selfless. She hadn't wanted to be the cause of a family breaking up, in the same way hers had fragmented in her childhood. He could only respect that choice. So the potentially life-changing words had remained in his head while her spirit had taken residence in his heart. This flirtation with temptation had shaken Addi. He hadn't seen it coming. He had never thought anyone could be so close an equal of his wife. And when he stood back, that is all she was, close to an equal. Different, but only nearly equal in measure on any scale. It was more the flattery of the situation which had temporarily affected his rationality, elevating the situation beyond what it really was. What it could only ever be. A fantasy.

What hurt the most was his guilt of courting the fantasy. He loved his wife and family so deeply that any thought of them being hurt by his hand made tears swell in his eyes. The spirit of that lady would remain in his heart, the same as the love of a lifelong friend, but the love of a partner had already been claimed by his wife. And the knowledge she was the custodian of that love brought him unimaginable joy.

COMING INTO THE LIGHT

I sat there staring at the tabletop and at my pint, which I'd barely touched. Reflecting on my thoughts, I felt more assured about taking a positive step forward. Feeling a quiet comfort with where I had eventually ended up tonight. Raising my head to look around the bar, I spied the landlord staring again. This time he decided not to smile, just peered back. A moment passed before he made a move, though this time it wasn't towards the far end of the bar. Instead, the gentleman moved to the counter hatch closest to me, raised it, passed through to the public area of the establishment and towards me. All the while I held his gaze, bemused by the approach.

"You alright sir?" The landlord enquired as he reached the booth.

"I'm good, thanks." I replied.

"Do you need me to get anyone for you?"

"No, I don't think so. I'm good." I was a little put out by the suggestion. "Why?"

The landlord looked hesitant to answer but, after some time, plucked up the nerve. "You've been sitting here talking to yourself for at least an hour now. I thought you were thinking out loud at first, but then it sounded like you were having a conversation with yourself."

I felt my face flush with embarrassment. "I'm sorry. I didn't realise I was talking out loud. My apologies."

"Just as long as you're alright!" And with that he returned to the bar to serve a customer.

I remained at the table. Sitting still, cradling what remained of my beer.

Alone.

REASSEMBLY

So who is Ethan?

He's the *me* I despise. The part of me I hate. My contemptible personality that I loathe the existence of and wish I could eradicate. On the days he is prevalent in my mind I can't stand the sight of me. He is my negativity sponge, concentrating rejection and despair like a magnifying glass with the sole aim to ignite depression. When he takes hold, shaking hopelessness is like trying to recover from the most aggressive virus.

I understand why he exists. Why I have manifested him in response to the path my life has taken. Everyone has a threshold. A tolerance to adversity beyond which they can't help but succumb to sadness. And in the past four years I've certainly received my fair share of mental blows and physical challenges. To help elevate myself from the doldrums when they arrive, I have started to think of Ethan as my personal *Marvin the Paranoid Android*. A parody of my depression. 'Life. Don't talk to me about life'. Somehow, seeing myself as a self-alienating, manic, depressive robot, has started to help me sidestep Ethan more often than not, and allow one of my more positive and productive personalities, such as Addi and Hawkshaw, to take residence for a while.

That doesn't mean I ignore 'failure' for want of a better word. All experience is an opportunity to learn. But I increasingly attempt to relegate disappointing outcomes to just that, an act of learning. Not as something to be relived to the point of wallowing in pity. The journey to self-awareness and self-actualisation is rarely straight forward for those that attain honest lasting change. And it isn't just knowledge of the words that makes the difference but belief in them. For that, we all have to go through a process, which takes time. So why do I find it so hard to deal with my Ethan? To explain that, I fear I must briefly retrace steps already recounted and explain the world in the light of a single being rather than a quintet of characters. And to simplify the summation further, I have parcelled it into three elements: career, health and family.

Live to work or work to live. That is the age-old query most people struggle with. We are conditioned in youth about the need to work and earn our keep. Survival is tough without money. And while there is much truth in that statement, it is also a doctrine that can lead to a path of servitude, of fearing job loss or striving for recognition in the workplace above all else. I've not succumbed to any of these symptoms in my life so far, and yet, until now, I have failed to acknowledge the importance of my career on my happiness.

For the first twenty years, my career went from strength to strength. Whilst it has been far from a perfect sequence of opportunities, through hard work I have been acknowledged and have ascended. And through uncompromising integrity I have subsequently been persecuted. Yet, no matter to which circumstance I have been periodically exposed, determination and grit have seen me through. My chronological employment status and remuneration have been like the teeth of a saw. I have pushed and elevated myself in numerous companies, only to be ousted by a fearful elderly peer who felt threatened by my presence twice, by a vindictive arrogant banker once, and by a politically-savvy friend and colleague once. Four career ostracisations in fifteen years. And every one of them discharged by unscrupulous *prosholes* who, bizarrely enough, had all managed to set me up while I was on holiday, serving up the ultimate return-to-work meeting invitation. It wasn't a surprise after such experiences that I had decided to become my own employer for a while. At least, that way, I had nobody else to blame but myself. Which is probably why after four years of fighting for short-term contracts while simultaneously trying to find my next corporate job, I feel like I have let myself down. And when hope faltered and doubt began to set in, depression was close at hand. After all, 'hope is the greatest depressant'.

Overlaying my career volatility has been a sequence of health matters. The fortune teller said I would pass through a period of health complications and as with many of her prophecies, she was right. I have repeatedly received poor liver and kidney function test results, which have led to several unsuccessful bouts of sobriety, the stresses and strains of my volatile career repeatedly requiring a vent. Each time the all clear had been given by a medical practitioner following further investigations. However, while the last investigations under my private medical plan reassuringly replicated the primary diagnosis regarding my kidneys and liver, less comfortingly it identified a second cause for concern in the process. My blood contained low-level traces of a protein associated to the development of cancer. Thus, today, my general practitioner annually performs tests to check for this as well as for my liver and kidney degradation.

Alongside the physical issues have been my psychological challenges. While these aren't considered medical to most, they are, and for me they have manifested in physical issues which have plagued my fragility further. While Tif may not exist and represents only the most desperate of thoughts, his erectile dysfunction was real and required acknowledgment. At my health centre in room 42, a room I'll always remember because of the number's infamy as the answer to the ultimate question of 'the meaning of life, the universe and everything?', I had met an attractive twenty-something medical student, blonde, svelte, and robed in scrubs. If Tif had been present in my psyche at the time, he'd probably have quipped. 'The number 42 really did lead to the answer to the meaning of life, the universe and everything!'. But he wasn't, and I had to disclose my flaccid personal problem to a very attractive doctor. Probably one of the greatest tests of confidence in my life.

The conversation had been stilted, and had been more a monologue from me to her. While training to practice one of the most personal of professions, she had struggled to forge a line of query she found comfortable uttering, so I filled her silence with a description of successful morning wood, through to an inability to rise in the presence of my wife. At times I could feel Tif quipping in my head, 'Ask her to take her clothes off and we can illustrate the problem!'

The young doctor had mercifully been saved from her awkwardness by the entrance of my usual doctor, also a lady. Some guys may find that difficult to embrace, but the honest truth is that I have always felt more at ease with female medical professionals than male. Their communication has always felt more considered, less superior and more understanding than my experience of their masculine counterparts. That said, open dialogue with two attractive doctors about having a droopy cock was virgin territory. Anyway, the consultation led to further blood tests which highlighted little other than a testosterone level at the lower end of the spectrum. Which can lead to issues getting erections, reduced sperm production, difficulty sleeping, diminished sex drive, depleted energy levels and mood swings. All of which I identified with.

I'm a root-cause person though. It's that engineering background again. I may not know biology, but a chemical mechanical structure is just that. Whether human or constructed. Failures in the system are either created or inherent in design. As a consequence of my appetite for understanding, I have researched the proven and potential links between depression and testosterone, but have drawn a blank. Both yield similar symptoms, but depression cannot trigger lower testosterone. However, a symptom of low testosterone is the fostering of depression. I have laboured over my recent history to see if I could identify a pattern that supported my symptoms. Where I have ended up is acceptance of an emotional cause. My mental state, physically manifesting itself. Psychological impotence. Not the answer I had hoped for, but a diagnosis I had half-expected. And probably the toughest diagnosis to accept. Psychological impotence affects one-in-five males under the age of fifty. A condition where the signals from the brain to the body to drive blood into the *corpus cavernosum*, or erectile tissue for the novice, swelling it to its maximum stretch, are disrupted. There are numerous causes for this. Stress and anxiety, depression, performance anxiety, guilt, low self-esteem. The list goes on. Yet, while holding a list of actors for my condition is useful, the challenge is accepting that the only cure is myself. I have to find a pathway for contentment. A path of raised spirits. Otherwise the cycle won't be broken. Depression feeding impotence. Impotence feeding guilt. Guilt feeding depression.

Enriched by Love

I have explained how my career led me to a path of self-doubt and depression. The more astute may guess that in absence of date-stamping, there is uniformity of frequency between redundancy and my repeated liver and kidney investigations. Now I don't know if that is real or not, but it is a correlation that can't be discounted. The ever more astute will also recognise that the suite of causes for my psychological impotence are all symptoms of my depression. I see these associations clearly and I know what I need to do, but am inadvertently impeded in relaunching myself this time. By what, do I hear you enquire?

For this I introduce the family dynamic. Those times before me when Hawkshaw stepped in and launched valiantly and defiantly forward, my three kids were young. With youth their needs were simple and their compliance reliable. Don't get me wrong, I adore my children. I love them without measure or expectation of reciprocation. I believe childhood is a gift that all should have the opportunity to savour. It's probably why I do challenges to raise money for a UK children's charity. And for a stable mind, continuation of such selfless support for my kids would be simple. But in the clutches of depression, stealing myself to continue to place their needs above mine depletes my energy, preventing escape from my own prison. I can recover my career. I can resolve to live a healthier life. But at times I have struggled to do these things while being a devoted father of three teenage daughters.

In the same four years of declining mental health, my eldest has annually fought with self-confidence over her academic capabilities. She has had numerous relationships, the last one of which apparently was so life changing, that 'I couldn't possibly understand'. So meteoric she had to revisit it three times before seeing the toxicity I had seen at its first termination. She has since lamented that poisonous relationship for twelve months like it was a life-affecting trauma rather than simply accepting she had poor judgement and he was a wanker. In the end though, to her credit, she has emerged stronger.

Then there's my middle daughter. She has issues, but I rarely know what they are. She is such an introvert that facts are verbalised only out of necessity. I sometimes feel she avoids discussion and debate because of the explosive conversations she has witnessed between myself and her elder sister. In the same way that I couldn't avoid the need for conflict with my eldest to keep her sane and confident, I can't ignore the unspoken needs of my middle daughter either, for fear of what they may mutate and manifest into if unchecked. She has such potential, and the world needs to see what she can achieve.

As for my youngest, she is a trooper. She just gets on and seems to walk the straight and narrow effortlessly. If she brings me anything, it is guilt. Not that she would want that. But I am usually so tired from parenting her elder siblings that there are days I have had little composure left for her, lest I plunge myself deeper into despair.

So how do I go about changing myself? That's the question I have tussled with. What I know is that whatever the solution, the love of and for my wife will be a central component. Though it becomes harder to continue relying on her for support with each day. We have been so close for so long that it is inevitable the mood of one instantaneously affects the other at a sub-conscious level. While I may be the one directly affected, I know all I do tugs at her core. I don't have an answer to that, all I can do is thank her for everything she has done and will do to help me. If such thanks ever took the form of a letter, it would read like this:

Dear Jenny,

There can never be enough words to explain how much you mean to me. Love is used too frequently to describe a point of acceptance by people for a state of settling. A word to brand their unity with positivity, even if the foundations are weak. That is not us. Our meeting was an event so rare that few realise the enormity of it. Fail to see how precious it was. But we do.

There was something between us from the very start. From the first time our eyes met. It was that sensation which gave me the resolve to walk slower and let you catch up with me that morning, going to university. It was that same feeling which gave me the gumption to come and ask if you wanted to talk that night in our study halls. It was that instantaneous fire which drew me to you.

People refer to such circumstance as a 'click' or a 'spark', but the sentiment is so much deeper and richer with us. There was anxiety, uncontrollable joy and desire, all wrapped in a snug blanket of friendship from those first words. An unimaginable sense of unity and, with it, any thought of separation banished.

We have seen and shared so much in our thirty years together that my memories fill a lifetime. I am still enraptured by you and cherish the journey we are sharing, craving to create more memories to fill my head to the brim.

In suffering and in pain, we have held each other together and come out stronger. When external volatile and tumultuous factors have laid siege, we have united to evade and stave off the worst, always emerging unscathed. In times of despair, we have turned to each other to find nothing but trust and relentless support. We are more than each other's rock. We are each other's foundations and, as such, form a unified body that cannot be shaken.

While we have suffered blows, individually and collectively at the hands of others, the abundance of reflection I carry with me every day is joyous. From dancing at discos, to driving in our underwear through Death Valley. From the birth of our children and watching them grow and challenge the world more vigorously than we did in our youth, to trekking the Andes and watching the dawn break through the Sun Gate at Machu Pichu. Moments of quiet, watching you sleep. Moments of laughter as we debated whether the sonic boom that reverberated through our house was a substation exploding, a nuclear bomb or our eldest daughter falling out of bed. Moments with friends and with family that drew both the best and the worst from us. So many memories you'd think we could grow tired of each other's company, but no. Every morning I wake up next to you, I thank the Lord for one more day in your company and I start to plan all the things we have yet to do.

I know, my love, that these recent years have not been my best. They have been darkened by my gloom. Frustrated by my splintered personality. For that, I will be forever sorry, because I can't give you those days back. I can neither replace nor upgrade those memories. Yet, while I have felt the guilt of a chalice weighing you down, you have risen each day to look on me with unfathomable pools of affection. You will never know how humbling that has been and how it spurs me to recovery.

My life is blessed for having you in it. And I will never take for granted the unconditional support you have gifted me. You are my friend. My companion. My lover. My lobster.

Your devoted husband

Profiling the Collective

So who am I?

That is the challenge I wake up to every day. Who am I going to be today? What am I going to do? This is my repetitive ritual of taking the blank canvas of my deflated soul and creating a vision of me. It is a delicate balance fed by the smallest externalities, the tiniest acts and influences. The wrong word from my wife, cleaning up my kids' spilled milk from the breakfast table, fumbling a glass in the sink as I wash it or stubbing my toe. The slightest detail could disintegrate the fragile positivity that I cloak myself in and send my day spiralling into a progression of meaningless and wasteful acts designed solely to avoid confrontation of dealing with the real issues that eclipse my happiness.

At this time, I am conscious that my mind has disaggregated into five skewed personalities that reflect my primary responses to the world around me. I think of them as coping mechanisms for the seemingly relentless adversity. These voices trapped in my head are both my confidants and my demons. And, collectively, they are my advisors. A governing council of my own fragmented construct. I know that, and every day I want to eliminate and merge them back into a single functional soul. To make them whole. Reconstitute them into the man I used to be. But something prohibits me. Stands in my path. An unseen obstacle that I persist in failing to identify, no matter how hard I analyse my actions and thoughts.

This is where Ethan is strongest. He is my victim. Not a defeatist, but a realist who favours observation of the downside. He is where my soul regresses when I want to ignore accountability for my life. Not a personality that wallows in self-pity as such. Though he is the me most susceptible to depression. The one that fails to see those invisible obstacles in my path, because he is one of them. The one who ceases to see the incredible life I have been blessed with. The one my other personalities endlessly conspire to change.

In stark contrast, there is Tif. He is the escapist and fantasist in me. A subversive narrative hidden in my subconscious, I believe partly conjured up to compensate for my physical impediment. A make-believe world conceived to protect my male pride and offer a sense of control to the decaying reality. But an uncontrolled fantasy that I acknowledge has swelled to affect the goodness inside me. To hold temptation before Addi's eyes, luring him toward a perceived temporary elation in exchange for the lasting damnation of guilt.

Tif is the addict I have feared I may become for so long, in some vain attempt to shore up my Maslow foundations through sexual gratification. The gypsy fortune-teller in New Orleans had been right about the impact of femininity in my life. It wasn't just constrained to the wealth of pheromones growing within my family. I love women. Love their form. Their personalities. Their smell. Their movement. A woman can become the sole vessel to deliver ultimate soulful sustenance. Offering physical encounters that suppress the testosterone cravings that too frequently distract me and might allow focus to be brought back to everything else in my life. Back to dealing with my existence. But such respite would be a double-edged sword. Impermanent peace served up by the hands of lasting guilt.

I have to confess, I have walked too close to that door of temptation once, and have feared that one day my moral resolve would permanently fail me and guilt would be embraced willingly as an inconsequential side effect. What it took me a while to appreciate fully was how much energy fighting this fantasy addiction was drained from my real battle with poor mental health. Addiction is a symptom of depression that offers a quick fix, whatever that fix may be. While that momentary euphoria may overpower the incessant destructive emotions of depression, it will change nothing.

Tif, like any person transformed by addiction, is a grotesque aberration of the human they consume. Divisive and deviant he has been a distasteful companion to my saner mind with its sturdier moral footing. And looking back at the depths of my depression, it scares me how close to the surface I let him reside. However, I take strength from the fact that at no time did I allow my addiction to overwhelm my beliefs. And when I have taken a moment to reflect with greater scrutiny the progression of Tif's subversive narrative, it reveals a comforting truth. A reality that while in despair Addi may have slipped towards temptation, in the end it was him that educated Tif to realise intimacy was best savoured, when infused with heartfelt affection.

Which brings me to Addi. Harbouring my compassion and empathy, he is the manifestation of my love. First and foremost, the love of a father I endeavour to be. If I consider myself to have had one success in life so far, that I have reflected on during my extended period of confusion, it is that I have, I believe, managed to be the best father I could have been. Of course, I try each day to be better, knowing that in the developing binary mind of a child, events and memories are either positive or negative, and the ability to change what has past is non-existent. Memories will be forged and survive their childhood. With the human capacity to recall hardships more than pleasures, the demand to deliver positive interaction and experience increases daily, hourly and by minute as they have approached adulthood and the concurrent release from my influence.

A little like Newt, Addi could be considered an internal construct created by external influences. My parents. I may have diminished their contribution to my growth at times, yet they never failed to offer unconditional love. As a child, it can be challenging to open your mind wide enough to witness the love, affection and support a good parent provides. But when parenthood arrived for me, the prism through which my life was viewed turned to illuminate their selflessness. It is an oddity of age that, in youth, humanity tends to take for granted the unseen care that shrouds them, protecting them from harm. But in the depths of adulthood, such watchfulness can be recalled to make the grief of losing a parent so acute. The knowledge of this care returning through concentrated recollections of shared moments that will never be repeated. These repressed memories of care swelling affection and elevating the heart to new heights, only to amplify the despair of loss. I was fortunate to see the end coming with my father. To have had the opportunity to recall those memories with him and to thank him for everything. I am equally fortunate to still have my mother with me. In me, Addi is the personality who feels pain the most. He is also the one with the strongest grasp on what is important in life. Love.

Then there is Newt. The personification of my wife, Jenny. An image of my longest standing real friend and life-long lobster. The person I have turned to for guidance and support in every challenge and endeavour I have attempted or dealt with. Jenny is for the most part perfect, and the times where she becomes less than that, I have had to acknowledge my influence, contributing to her mental fatigue in being there for me. Something which must have been incredibly difficult to do when I have been at my lowest ebb, making it increasingly hard for me to stand there and acknowledge time after time that recently my effect on her has been less than positive. That I may have hurt the one I love. While never deliberate, these failings of loving demonstration inevitably open the door to my guilt. It takes a resilient mind to accept such inadequacy and not surrender to despair. The fact that Newt exists inside my mind is a testament to how much I cherish my wife. A demonstration of how much I value her thoughts. How much of me has become us during our years together. Newt is a constant reminder of Jenny's unwavering belief in me.

Finally, there is Hawkshaw. The man I mostly am. I know that. I am not a victim of my life, I am just allowing myself to feel as though I am under sustained embattlement, absent of control. Surrounded by a myriad of external gatekeepers seeking to define my future deliberately or otherwise, with the same effect, my isolation. The Hawkshaw inside me knows that this is just the way the world is. Too many in power use their status to restrain others. I have seen it many times before, and I prevailed. In life, I have challenged and pushed my body in every way possible, opposing these self-ordained jailers to my growth. I acknowledge that, in my career, my present predicament is part borne from that passion for a meaningful existence. An unwillingness to conform where a better avenue may exist. A refusal to ignore my generation's impact on the quality of life for generations to come. A belligerent aversion to accept the aging process and its effects on my body, pushing myself towards tougher challenges to extend my capacity for life and the savouring of all this world has to offer. No matter how low I have felt, I would not change this part of me. I do not live with regret from my own choices, because to do so would inevitably mean surrendering the merits of the resultant experiences. But as with any life, some experiences are negative and from these I aspire to learn.

To the outside world, Tif, Newt, Hawkshaw and Addi have been the external faces I present. Tif, the sexually overt, anecdotal story-telling entertainer. Newt, the structured, methodical intellectual. Hawkshaw, the confident, strong entrepreneur and adventurous challenger. And Addi, the compassionate, affectionate and loving family man. While Ethan has been the face I wear inside. The one I dare not display for fear of judgement. My inner disappointment.

So who am I?

I am Grant.

THE STRONGER SEX

That day, I left the pub slightly embarrassed that my self-administered psychology had been disturbingly witnessed by the landlord. Not concerned that someone had noticed, that actually felt good. In fact, it felt absurdly reassuring that I could still be seen. That other humans still acknowledged me and I hadn't completely vanished from humankind's perception. I wasn't the ghost I feared. No, the embarrassment I felt was not the observation itself, but the interpretation of my ramblings. The level of mental health cognisance by the general public is limited. Even science considers it an area of development. A new frontier.

To watch from afar, a person holding a conversation with themselves may be considered quirky. To be in audible range and hear the narrative, hear the multiple distinct characters being portrayed, may lead most people to diagnose ineptly such behaviour as schizophrenia or dissociative identity disorder. And for some people that might be true. For me it isn't. I am conscious of taking my own counsel. Aware that my friends are not real, but are creations of my own making, existing to help me understand and manage my behaviour. That they have been born to gift myself identity. To deliver clarity to the splintered mind that I own. Each personality exhibits specific clusters of traits and thoughts that I portray at different times in response to external factors affecting me. In this regard, together they seek to help me find a cohesive individual that my true self, the consolidated personality of all five creations, can arbitrate with to find a path forward. It is like my brain is comprised of a quintet of distinct molecules that are held together by bonds to form a single compound. Me.

Occasionally, the external environment has a direct impact on the stability of the compound, preferentially reacting with one molecule and straining the bonds that hold it fast. Forces endeavouring to overpower the bond's elasticity and irreversibly break the molecule free, creating a free radical, so to speak. Once free, such radicals are highly volatile, exhibiting extreme characteristics, leading to two or more independent personalities constrained within a single body, unable to reconstitute themselves. Continuously pitting themselves against each other in a struggle for dominance.

I have never been stretched that far in my fight. My mind has never been broken in two or more pieces. I have felt the strain, though. Felt the all-consuming fatigue of a struggle for balance and objectivity. So where has all my self-destructive behaviour led me? That is the question. Or more specifically, what have I learnt that will help me move forward? That will aid me in marginalising Tif and Ethan and progress balanced between Hawkshaw, Addi and with a dash of Newt? The answer is not simple. They rarely are. But it may be characterised through existential observation.

A 'good life' isn't about the pursuit of wealth, or power, or glory. It's not even about the quantity of friends I have or colleagues that respect and admire me. I don't need reverence. I don't need to leave a mark on the world in the traditional construct of fame. No. For me, a 'good life' has become about how I feel about myself. How I appreciate myself. How I value myself. It is personal and can't be measured against another person's perception of a 'good life'. Such other perceptions are unique and have evolved through an infinite number of nurturing pathways directed by family, friends, and peers. As has mine.

My benchmark for a good life is basic but it has been forged through a tortuous route of introspection. My scale is at the tip of the Maslow triangle. My scale informs me to look in the mirror each day and ask the question: Do I like the person I see? Do I accept who I am? Can I live with myself? The days that I respond with 'No', these are the days depression takes grip and suffocates my soul; and I have to fight the hopelessness before I can grapple with changing the causes of self-loathing. It's a debilitating fight for happiness. A battle for joy and contentment, where I play the role of a patient in post-operation recovery. My scars still tender, distinct and painful to view. The residual effect of the anaesthetic refusing to allow my thoughts to coalesce and become whole.

My family serves as the medical staff, tirelessly cheerful and optimistic that a complete return to my former health is inevitable and near at hand. None is trained to support such recovery procedure. They get no reprieve. No shift pattern to escape and revitalise themselves. They are imprisoned in continuous post-surgery care. Despite feeling captive, they take on the task without any sense of obligation, but instead full of unwavering compassion for me. I can attest that it's hard to accept the scale of this unconditional love at times when I feel so incapable of reciprocating fully.

On these worst days, I feel the shame and guilt of a succubus draining the life from them for my own survival. Using their strength as my foundation to ascend from the pit. These are the days I choose to forget. The days when the rain saturates my resolve, and the pit starts to collapse, the floor becoming a quagmire that envelops my feet and draws me deeper into the earth. I know these days for the darkness they bring. And while I may in my rationale times have never really come close to considering a premature departure from this world by my own hand, I have debated what impact my absence would truly bring. However, I have never allowed such thoughts to linger. Instead, I instigate the psychological coping strategy of becoming motionless in the bog, in an attempt to suppress the rate of descent and buy time for a solution to materialise. I regress into myself. I avoid human contact, finding a quiet corner and laying still on the ground with nothing but the drum and pound of my heart beating against the palm of my hands for company. I focus solely on the present. Sometimes recovery is in minutes, sometimes hours, but rarely days.

I attempt to avoid these days more and more. I try to gild myself before the day's challenges are presented. In the past year, I have endeavoured to focus on starting my days with realistic positivity to avoid receding into the mud and ensure each day leads me closer to exiting the pit. I wake with the birds, long before any of my slumbering family is likely to stir. I make myself a fresh cup of coffee and sit and watch the news in silence. I take this time to centre myself. I see the world in extremes. Structure and sanity pitted against chaos, greed and inhumanity. A frequently selfish world ignorant to the plight of their earthbound neighbours, and short-sighted to the impact their material obsessions have on the environmental inheritance being bestowed on future generations.

I see the world's turmoil and, in those moments, find perspective to my problems, which really are inconsequential first-world problems. I acknowledge that I am in the minority, not of tangible despair, but of birth privileges. I don't have to fight for life every day. My sole battle is a fight for the privilege to enjoy life. I greet my family with a smile when they descend the stairs. I see their beauty and their love, and I find it easier to accept the help they offer. I want to hug them and never let go. I want them to feel the depth of my appreciation, my gratitude for their unwavering support. They are the light that brightens my days. The flaming torch that licks and lashes the night air to brighten my path, revealing the way and leading me to sanctuary. They are my inspirational fellow travellers that bring joy to every breath and beauty to the world. This is how my good days start.

I have endeavoured to conjure suitable words to express how they make me feel. To tell them how much I love them always seems inadequate. Words capture moments in time, but once uttered, they are diluted by the air that embraces them. Words are like vapour, impossible to hold on to. But actions breed memories that may forever be reflected on. And embedded in those memories, emotions can be captured that retain sufficient potency to raise a smile, a laugh or well a tear. It is through such actions that I attempt to gild their future recall.

So as I push the door open and prepare to enter my home, I am determined to make things better. To be better. To make Jenny and my kids happier. I'll do that for them today. I'll commit my heart and soul to that endeavour. The same as I did yesterday. The same as I will do tomorrow. Because I love them fiercely. I'll always love them fiercely.

Back in New Orleans, the fortune-teller had told me my life would be bathed in femininity and she was right. Those in my life that I love the most and love me back with equal ferocity, are all fantastic women. My wife. My daughters.

Epilogue: The Fight for Light

If my story has felt fragmented... Disjointed... Disconnected... Jumpy... That's what it has been like inside my depressed mind. An almost uncontrollable, perpetual, dysfunctional narrative. Competing parallel conversations, all vying for dominance. At the centre of it has been a lone, rational voice endeavouring to unify thoughts and offer a way forward. A voice it has taken me three years to recoalesce.

Life is tumultuous. It doesn't matter how it is approached, life will bring surprises. All one can do is find the strength to react positively and refuse to let go of their destiny. However, take this short account of a part of my life as a warning: *Prosholes are real.*

They can be the court appointed administrators of this world. People who are entrusted and empowered to act with honesty and good faith, but whose wills are weak in the presence of commercial enterprise that they assume impunity. If you ever have the misfortune to meet one of these, have the presence of mind to hold their character into account for the integrity of the legal process they administer.

They can be the investment banker who uses other people's money to line their own pockets with gold, without risking capital of their own. Empowered God's gifted trust by their employers and void of authenticity, morals and ethics. Such contemptible humans, whose ability to tolerate themselves lays in flawed rules of governance created solely to accrue wealth for themselves, their lords and their masters. Never a thought spared for the workers whose toils deliver it. If you ever have the misfortune to meet one of these bankers, have the emotional composure to know there is nothing you can do. The herd will protect the herd. Just take notes. Keep records. And if they fuck up, take them to task. If not, pursue whatever means are available to you to hold them to account. If we accept such evil, it will multiply and become accepted as 'just the way things are'.

They can be friends who approach you for help and advice, assuming that friendship exempts them from offering equitable give-and-take remuneration. Individuals who believe that exploitation of generosity is a strength for them and weakness in others. These bullies will place the pursuit of their success ahead of any friendship, if that is what's required. If you ever encounter one of these in life, just have the objectivity to acknowledge they were never a friend to begin with and have the courage to let them go. It is the quality of friendship that counts, not the quantity.

They can be friends who place self-preservation ahead of your wellbeing. Individuals who would undermine your position if it meant they could achieve higher standing. These people are just sad. The only option available that avoids continued anger is to cut them out of your life like a cancer. Don't waste your efforts praying they will one day suffer a similar fate. Because to do so is to lower down to their level. Be better than that.

As individuals, we each hold a responsibility for how society evolves. If we accept *prosholes* without challenging them, such behaviour will be deemed acceptable and society will be further degraded. There is a long-standing belief that it takes courage to be bad. To break the rules. I contest that, because it takes far greater courage to remain good. To act with integrity no matter what the outcome is for yourself. This is the path I have always aspired to, but for it to be impactful a collective must be formed. *Prosholes* should not be tolerated. They should be exposed for the abuse they perpetrate in the workplace. So act with integrity.